THE VAMPI

THE VAMPIRE VANISHES

Willis Hall

ILLUSTRATED BY
TONY ROSS

RED FOX

A Red Fox Book

Published by Random House Children's Books
20 Vauxhall Bridge Road, London SW1V 2SA

A division of Random House UK Ltd
London Melbourne Sydney Auckland
Johannesburg and agencies throughout the world

3 5 7 9 10 8 6 4 2

First published in Great Britain by
The Bodley Head Children's Books 1995
Red Fox edition 1996

This Red Fox edition 1997

Printed and bound in Great Britain by
Cox & Wyman Ltd, Reading, Berkshire

Papers used by Random House UK Limited
are natural, recyclable products made from wood grown in
sustainable forests. The manufacturing processes conform to
the environmental regulations of the country of origin.

RANDOM HOUSE UK Limited Reg. No. 954009

ISBN 0 09 922142 X

1

Once lit, the fire took hold and spread all too quickly.

Hungry tongues of red-and-orange flame shot up the ancient grey, stone, ivy-covered castle walls and licked around the parapeted ramparts. Occasionally, showers of sparks flew out from the flames and settled in the tops of the pine trees which surrounded the ancient building, starting small subsidiary fires of their own, until the entire mountainside, and the village nestling in the valley below, were bathed in the fiery glow. A figure appeared, briefly, peering out, horror-struck, through the leaded glass at one of the castle's topmost windows. For no more than a second, the man was clearly visible to the assembled crowd below. His face was pale and thin and, as his mouth opened wide with pain and terror, his two pointy teeth were plain to see. He let out a scream of anguish which could not be heard from behind the arched and mullioned window, then he too was gone, engulfed in the all-consuming flames.

A low murmur of grim satisfaction went up from the watching villagers.

"Death to Dracula!" announced Police Sergeant Kropotel, gruffly. As he slipped his monocle into his failing right eye, he added: "Thus perish all vampires."

1

"Thus perish all vampires!" echoed the villagers then, shouldering their makeshift weapons of scythes and pitchforks, they turned and set off down the steep mountain path towards the simple but welcoming comfort of their homes below.

As dawn's rosy fingers crept over the rim of the mountain top, two words were written in huge golden letters across the cloudless, early morning sky:

THE END

As the film's closing captions rolled on the jetliner's cinema screen, a ragged burst of applause rose up from the ranks of seated passengers.

"That was a bit of all right, Edith, and no mistake," said one returning holiday maker, turning to his wife who was sitting in a window seat. "Especially that bit where the vampire stuck his pointy teeth into that young lady's neck and all her blood spouted out," he added, enthusiastically.

"It certainly gave me the goose-bumps, Arnold," Edith agreed as she chewed on a salted nut. "I'm glad that Dracula got his come-uppance at the end though."

All of the passengers it seemed, with one exception, had thoroughly enjoyed the in-flight entertainment.

Sitting alone, halfway down the flight's No Smoking section, Count Alucard, the last remaining member of the Dracula line, shuffled uneasily in his seat. "I do think it's wrong of them to show horror films," he murmured to himself as he drained his glass of tomato juice. "Travelling by air is scary enough, without adding to the experience."

2

Tomato juice was Count Alucard's favourite tipple. Unlike his infamous ancestors, the Count was a vegetarian vampire. If and when he turned himself into a bat (which he was more than capable of doing), he became a fruit bat and not a bat of the blood-sucking variety. Even the sight of his own blood, should he chance to cut his finger or nick his chin while shaving, was sufficient to give him the shivers. And, although since early childhood he had displayed the same pale complexion, the same red-rimmed eyes as his vampire forbears, the very idea of lodging his teeth into a human being's neck was enough to make his Transylvanian toes curl up inside his immaculately polished shoes.

Perched on his airline seat, Count Alucard nervously fiddled with the buckle on his seat-belt and silently prayed that none of his fellow

passengers would recognise him. After having seen the in-flight movie, with all of its spooky vampire goings-on, they might very easily get the wrong idea about him and start to panic – and then anything might happen!

On more than one occasion in his life, the Count had been forced to flee from the wrath of ordinary folk who, without just cause and fearing for their lives, had driven him out of house and home and sought to kill him. Supposing his fellow passengers were to take similar thoughts into their heads? He would find that hiding places were in short supply on board the aircraft! And why shouldn't they, indeed? After all, there was more than his pale complexion and his pointy teeth to remind them of the vampire villain whose evil exploits they had been watching on the cinema screen – there was also the Count's choice of clothing.

While all of the other passengers – returning sun-bronzed holiday makers for the most part – were wearing wrinkled shell suits or T-shirts and scruffy jeans and the well-worn sneakers they found most comfortable to travel in, Count Alucard was dressed, as he always dressed, in his formal black suit, white starched frilly shirt, white bow tie, black silk socks and highly-polished black shoes. His long black cloak, with the crimson lining, was thrown carelessly across the empty seat beside him. He was also proud to wear a gold medallion, embossed with the family crest, on a fine gold chain around his neck.

Thus had his late father, the previous count, always seen fit to dress, and his father before him, and *his* father before him – indeed, all of his ancestors throughout Transylvanian history. And even though the present count did not share his forbears' taste for nocturnal bat-winged wanderings in search of blood, Count Alucard was not ashamed to dress in the manner which befitted the family name.

As the pretty airline hostess moved down the aisle, sliding up the window blinds and flooding the cabin with bright morning sunlight, Count Alucard cast a second nervous glance at his nearby fellow passengers. He was hoping against hope that they would not turn their attention on him. He was in luck! At that very moment, the pilot's voice came over the speakers, announcing that the aircraft would be arriving at its destination on schedule, in a matter of minutes, and advising one and all to "Fasten your seat-belts" and to "Return your seats to the upright position" in preparation for the landing. The Count was relieved to see that his fellow travellers were far too busy obeying these instructions – and far too excited at the prospect of touching down on solid ground – to pay him any attention.

Glancing down, out of the window, Count Alucard was both surprised and pleased to see that the aircraft had already descended from its cruising height. They had come down through a heavy bank of cloud and the north of England – or, at least, a goodly portion of it – was clearly visible some distance below.

Then, as the aircraft banked, Count Alucard's eyeline suddenly changed and, magically, the earth

5

below seemed that much closer. They were flying first over vast purple moors; then craggy hills; then farmsteads with green and golden fields the size of postage stamps and separated by ribbon-like roads. The ribbon roads twisted in and out of sprawling towns which were bordered by estates of houses which seemed to spread out without shape or purpose. They were flying low enough now for the Count to make out football grounds, parks, swimming pools, town halls and factory chimneys.

Count Alucard allowed himself a little smile. In one of those towns, on one of those estates, in one of those neat pinhead-sized houses, there lived a good friend that he knew he could always count upon.

"Henry Hollins!" Count Alucard murmured his friend's name softly, to himself, and his smile broadened. And why not? For when you are a Transylvanian vampire count – albeit a vegetarian one – good friends that can be counted upon are few and far between. The Count wondered whether Henry might have received his letter yet . . .?

"Oh dear, oh dear . . .!" the Count murmured to himself. Glancing down the aisle, his eyes had met those of a lady passenger who was sitting several rows in front of him. Stooping to pick up a fallen magazine, she had turned in her seat and, from the puzzled expression on her face, there could be no doubt that she was taking in his curious choice of clothing. With the vampire movie still in her mind, she was putting two and two together.

"An extremely pleasant morning to you, dear

lady!" said the Count in an attempt to calm her growing fears. "I trust I find you in the best of health?" he added in his most charming voice. Then, favouring her with his smile, he inclined his head politely.

The lady, still puzzled, managed a faint smile in return then, taking her eyes off the Count, she turned back in her seat and, thankfully, turned her thoughts to other matters.

"Thank goodness!" The Count breathed a small sigh of relief. Good manners, it seemed, had done the trick. They usually did, he told himself. But there were moments in a vampire's life when, he sometimes thought, as well as being able to transform oneself into a bat, it might prove useful if one was also granted the ability to make oneself invisible. . . .

"Abracadabra! Hocus Pocus! Your card has vanished completely!" announced Albert Hollins, waving his empty hands in front of his chest. "As you can see, Emily," he added, "I have nothing whatsoever up my sleeves."

"Except your arms," replied Mrs Hollins, giving their son, Henry, a mischievous wink.

"Very funny, Emily," said Mr Hollins sarcastically. He was standing with his back to the sitting-room fireplace. "Perhaps you'd like to swap places and do this trick instead of me?"

"No, thanks, Albert," said Emily, biting back a smile as she shook her head.

"Get on with it, Dad," urged Henry who was

eager to go out into the garden. Something very exciting had happened to him earlier that morning and, for the moment at least, he was hugging the secret to himself.

While both of his parents were still fast asleep, Henry Hollins had heard the postman's footsteps on the front garden gravel path. Leaping out of bed, slipping on his dressing-gown and hurrying downstairs, he had found an airmail letter, addressed to himself, lying on the doormat. The distinctive double-headed eagle on the Transylvanian stamp had left him in no doubt as to where and who the letter was from. He had opened the envelope excitedly and quickly scanned the contents. Count Alucard had written to tell him that he would shortly be arriving in England. But Henry had been forced to slip the letter into his pocket, half-read, at the sound of his father moving about upstairs. He was anxious now to get outside and into the privacy of the garden shed. Although he was not a secretive boy by nature, Henry had decided that he would like to study the letter in full before announcing its arrival to his parents – if he should decide to tell them about it at all.

Both Mr and Mrs Hollins had met Count Alucard on several occasions. They were in no way disapproving of him – indeed they had gone out of their way to help him more than once[1] – but Henry had come to realise that when you have a Transylvanian vampire Count for your best friend, it is wisest not to keep reminding your parents of

[1] See *The Last Vampire* and *The Vampire's Holiday*.

8

that fact. Mums and dads, as Henry knew well, are inclined to fret over little things like that.

"I'll start again," said Albert Hollins reproachfully, taking a pack of cards out of his cardigan pocket. He fanned them out in both of his hands in front of his wife and son who were perched, side by side, on the edge of the sofa. "Choose a card, Emily – any card," said Albert.

Emily stared hard at the backs of the playing cards for several seconds then, reaching out a hand, plucked one out, nervously, and held it up to her face. "The Eight of Clubs," she said.

"No, no, no, Emily," said Albert, slightly vexed. "You mustn't tell me what it is – you're going to put it back into the pack and I'm going to find it. Start again – only this time keep it to yourself."

Emily, who had things to do about the house, sighed, but did as she had been asked. Albert Hollins, it should be said (and Emily often said it), was 'magic-mad these days'.

From Monday to Friday, every week of the year (holidays excepted), Albert Hollins worked in the packing office at the Staplewood Garden Gnome Company Ltd. The factory was situated on the outskirts of the small town where the Hollins family lived and, as its name suggested, manufactured jolly, white-bearded, red-cheeked garden gnomes in all shapes and sizes. Staplewood garden gnomes were famous not only in the United Kingdom, but in all four corners of the world. They were even to be found in the Buckingham Palace Royal Gardens. Albert Hollins had been at the garden gnome factory for all of his working life. He had been given a job there as office boy and general dogsbody when he had left school and had risen, through the years, to the important post of Assistant Head of the Packing and Despatch Department.

But at the time that this particular tale begins, if garden gnomes provided the bread-and-butter of the Hollins's family life, it was magic tricks that made Albert Hollins's life worth living. Quite simply, in the words of Mrs Hollins, her husband was 'magic-mad'. Magic had not been his hobby for very long, but already it was close to becoming an obsession.

So much so, that it was beginning to cause Mrs Hollins slight anxiety. Household tasks which Albert had previously tackled with enthusiasm, these days went untackled. Weeds flourished on the Hollins's once well-trimmed and weed-free lawn. Two tins of glossy white paint, purchased several months before in the local DIY store and intended to be spread across the bathroom walls, lay unopened in the garage, gathering dust. A wooden shelf, which Albert had put up before Christmas (and which had come undone at one end in the second week of January), hung dangerously askew over the kitchen work-top.

What was worse, Emily not only had to suffer her husband's present lack of interest in domestic matters, she was also expected to be his willing stooge whenever he learned (or *thought* that he had learned), a new magic trick. Just as she was doing at that very minute.

Having gone through the rigmarole of choosing an entirely different card for the third time that morning, Emily glanced at it and, this time without announcing its identity, returned it to the other fifty-one playing cards in Albert's hands. Albert shuffled the pack energetically and then selected one from the middle and set it down on the coffee table, face up, under Emily's nose.

"There!" he announced triumphantly. "Your card!"

Emily Hollins stared hard and long at the Three of Diamonds for several seconds and then shrugged her shoulders, uncertainly. "I don't know, Albert," she said at last. "It might have been the Three of Diamonds – then again, it might not."

"How do you mean, 'It *might* have been'?" asked Albert, slightly peevishly. "Either it is your card or it isn't, Emily."

"I know," admitted Emily. "But I'm afraid I've forgotten what my card was. It might easily have been that one, if you say so, Albert – then again, it might have been the Four of Diamonds. Or was it the Jack of Clubs?"

"You know what your problem is, Emily, don't you?" said Albert, getting more peeved by the second. "You don't pay attention. Okey-dokey, we'll start all over again. Only this time, Henry gets to pick the card." Albert fanned out the cards once more, face down. "Choose a card, Henry. Any card. But don't tell me what it is . . .*Henry*!"

"Sorry, Dad!" said Henry, with a start. "Did you say something?"

Henry had been paying even less attention than his mother. Some moments before, out of the corner of his eye and through the sitting-room window, he had glimpsed a low-flying jetliner making its approach to the busy airport situated outside a large industrial city to the north of Staplewood. Day-dreaming, Henry had begun to wonder whether the aircraft might be the very one that was bringing Count Alucard to England? But, no, he told himself. There were dozens – perhaps hundreds – of jetliners flying in and out of the airport every day. It would be too much of a coincidence. It was, after all, only an idle day-dream.

But sometimes, what might seem like an idle day-dream can prove to be a rock-solid real-life fact. . .

"Mercy me!" Count Alucard murmured to himself nervously, as he dabbed at his pale, perspiring forehead with the spotless white silk handkerchief

12

which he had taken out of his top pocket. He shuffled his smartly-shod feet impatiently on the floor of the airport's arrivals area. He was waiting for his belongings to arrive on the luggage carousel and doing his best to ignore the several curious glances being cast in his direction.

Not that the Transylvanian count could ever find it in his generous heart to blame his fellow travellers for turning their inquisitive glances on him. After all, as he himself was always the very first to admit, his distinctive style of dress did tend to make him stand out in a crowd.

Happily, moments later, the terminal luggage conveyor juddered into life. Count Alucard let out a small sigh of relief when his shiny, smooth black coffin was the very first item to appear on the moving belt. As he stepped forward to claim his solitary piece of luggage, several of the returning holiday-makers nervously wheeled their empty trolleys out of his path.

One lady, however, wearing a floppy T-shirt decorated with a colourful parrot, a pair of red-and-yellow striped tight cotton trousers, flip-flops and a straw sun-hat, remained exactly where she stood, too transfixed with fear to shift so much as a finger. It was the same woman, Count Alucard remembered, who had glanced at him across the aircraft's aisle. Frozen, her mouth wide open, she had her eyes glued on the sinister-looking polished coffin which was gliding towards her on the luggage carousel.

"Pray excuse me, dear lady," the Count murmured into her ear, politely. "And do allow me

to assure you that there is no cause whatsoever for the slightest concern," he added as, in one brisk movement, he took hold of two of the coffin's silver handles, hauled it from off the moving belt and stood it upright on the floor. For although the coffin was a heavy item, Count Alucard had manhandled it with an ease which had been born of long experience. He had been taking the smart black casket around the world with him on his many travels over a number of years.

Vampires, as everyone knows, can only manage to sleep properly when they are cosily tucked up in their coffins with the lids shut tight. They sleep through the daylight hours and spend their nights as blood-drinking bats, fluttering restlessly around the earth in search of human necks into which they can sink their pointy teeth. All vampires, that is, except Count Alucard. When that Transylvanian nobleman turns into a bat, he much prefers a ripe nectarine, or a fleshy peach, or – best of all – a nice juicy blood orange, in preference to the taste of human blood. For this reason, he has long since given up the unsociable habit of taking wing by night and sleeping through the day. Although, it must be stated, he still prefers his satin-sheeted, cosily padded coffin to sleeping in a proper bed.

"The plain fact of the matter, dear friend," he will politely explain to anyone who cares to ask, waving his pale and delicate hands in the air as he speaks, "is that I simply cannot get a good night's sleep in a strange bed. I just toss and turn and fidget and lie awake for hour after hour.

15

It's *too* distressing for words!"

All of which goes some way towards explaining why the Count had arrived in company with his coffin in the luggage collection area of the airport's Terminal Two.

"Thank goodness for that, dear lady," he said with a reassuring smile to the lady in the T-shirt as he glanced at the luggage label which was tied securely to one of the coffin's finely worked coffin handles. "It *is* my coffin. It would have been most uncivil of me to have gone off with someone else's by mistake."

The lady, still lost for words, did her very best, but without much success, to manage a smile in return. Count Alucard snapped his heels together and gave her another polite bow then, balancing his coffin carefully on top of his airport trolley, he set off towards Customs and the Nothing To Declare Green Exit.

The lady, whose name was Mrs Sylvia Cresswell, gave a little shiver and wondered, for a moment, whether she might be dreaming? "Oooh!" she murmured as she pinched her upper left arm and assured herself that she was most definitely wide awake.

She had, she told herself, just met a real live vampire. She wondered how she had managed to remain so calm throughout the encounter? Not only *how*, but *why*? Of course, she knew now what she *should* have done. She should have opened her mouth, wide, and screamed and screamed until someone came to her assistance. Never mind. She had the monster's *exact* description etched on her

16

memory – right from his jet-black, slicked back hair down to the pointed toes of his shiny black shoes.

Should she ever have the misfortune to encounter the evil monster again, she would know *exactly* what to do.

2

"Crikey Moses – what's your game, chum?" gulped Customs Officer Hilton Hargreaves, very nearly swallowing his chewing-gum in surprise as Count Alucard and his coffin hove into view. "And just where do you think you're going with that?"

"Why – through there, officer," replied the Count, fluttering his long fingers in the direction of the public lounge.

"Oh no, you're not, matey!" stuttered the young Customs man. "Not before I've given that coffin a thorough going-over. What do you think you're up to, anyway – wheeling a coffin through Customs?" He paused as an awful, horrid thought occurred to him and then added in a frightened whisper: "You . . .you haven't got a thingummy . . .a dead person inside it, have you?"

"Certainly not!" snapped the Count. "As if I would! Why, the very idea!"

"Well, what's it for then? Come on, quickly, tell me!"

But Count Alucard did not reply immediately. He hung his head, shuffled his feet and thought very hard. He had landed himself in a rather tricky situation. If he told the Customs man the truth and owned up to being a Transylvanian vampire count – albeit a vegetarian one – he would be in all kinds of trouble. He knew, from many years of experience, that the Customs man would raise an immediate alarm. Why, the very mention of the word 'vampire' was sufficient to send most uniformed officials into a state of instant panic: ringing alarm bells; blowing whistles which summoned more officials – and, as likely as not, the Count would find himself handcuffed and behind bars without any further questions being asked. On the other hand, Count Alucard was a truthful person. It was not in his nature to tell lies if he could possibly help it.

"Come on! Come on! Speak up!" continued Customs Officer Hargreaves, his hand already hovering over the pocket which contained his whistle.

"Pray do allow me to assure you, officer," began the Count at last, choosing his every word carefully and speaking in his usual well-mannered tones, "that there is nothing either untoward or illegal inside this coffin. Indeed, had I thought myself to be in possession of anything that might be considered questionable in the slightest way whatsoever, I would have made my way through the corridor marked Goods To Declare."

"Oh yes," sniffed Hargreaves, disbelievingly. "And how many times a day do you think that I hear that one?"

To give the Customs officer his due, he was not enjoying the best of mornings.

Things had begun to go wrong for him at

breakfast-time. He had come down from the bathroom, his Paisley-patterned dressing-gown over his blue-and-white stripey pyjamas, only to discover that his mother had over-cooked his boiled egg. The yolk had not been runny enough for Hilton Hargreaves to dip his toasted soldiers into it. He had been forced to eat the egg with a teaspoon and munch the soldiers separately. And, as if that had not been a bad enough beginning to the day, he had realised, once he was on the bus, that he had forgotten to change out of his slippers into his Customs officer's regulation black shoes before leaving home.

What was worse though – much worse – was that what he was wearing on his feet was no ordinary pair of slippers. If only they had been! But no, they were a pair which had been given to him, on his last birthday, by his Aunt Edith. She had bought them in the gift shop of a safari park that she had recently visited. They were furry black-and-white slippers and each of them had a perky panda's face embroidered on the front. From his trouser turn-ups upwards, Hilton Hargreaves considered himself a smartly turned-out Customs officer; but from his ankles down, he felt himself to be a disgrace to his uniform.

On top of which, he was also a figure of fun. He felt sure that it had been his footwear that had caused two airline stewards to giggle behind his back in the Customs officers' washroom earlier, even though they had shaken their heads and blinked in wide-eyed innocence when he had turned from the wash basin and accused them of

so doing. "I can't see anything to snigger about," he had told them, adding: "In any case, you two shouldn't be in here at all. It's for Customs officers only – it says so on the door." Then, when he had turned again to dry his hands on the roller-towel, he could have sworn that one of them had softly blown a raspberry in his direction.

It was hardly surprising, then, that Customs Officer Hargreaves was not in the best of tempers on that particular morning. It was just unfortunate that Count Alucard was the one that was having to suffer for it.

"We'll have that coffin up on the counter, as quickly as you please!" growled the Customs officer. "Open up the lid and let's be seeing what you've got inside."

"My dear young man, I am only too happy to oblige," murmured the Count, hoisting the coffin from off the trolley and onto the inspection counter with the same ease that he had lifted it up from the luggage carousel. He tugged at the heavy polished lid which opened with an eerie creak that sent goose-pimples up, then down, the Customs officer's spine.

One by one, the Count lifted out the items which were in the coffin and laid them neatly, in a row, on the counter.

The coffin's satin-lined interior held all of those personal belongings which the Count considered essential for an overseas journey: a couple of starched white frilly-fronted shirts, both bearing the monogram 'C-A'; several items of white silk underwear, similarly embroidered; a pair of crimson pyjamas with the same family crest on the jacket pocket; some pairs of black silk socks; a toilet-bag for his toothbrush, toothpaste, shaving things and a bottle of his favourite aftershave, *Transylvanian Dawn*, which smelled both of pine trees in the early morning and woodland bracken heavy with dew; a six-pack of cans of tomato juice; some embrocation, containing secret ingredients, to keep his parchment-like bat-wings supple; and, last but by no means least, the latest issue of *The Coffin-Maker's Journal* (which was his constant bedside reading).

Customs Officer Hilton Hargreaves pursed his lips, frowned, and studied all of these items in turn, without saying a word.

"May I put them back now, please?" asked the

Count, politely, when he judged that the Customs man had completed his inspection.

"Certainly not!"

"May I ask, *why* not?"

"Empty your pockets first."

Count Alucard sighed, but did as he was told. He laid out the contents of his pockets alongside the items from the coffin: his wallet; his cheque book from the Bank of Transylvania; his passport; his airline ticket; his bunch of keys including the clumsy, iron-cast ancient key that turned the lock of Castle Alucard's iron-studded oak front door.

There was not one single item to which the Customs officer could raise the slightest objection, but he did not appear any happier. "It all seems very suspicious to me," he grumbled. "How am I to know that there isn't a secret panel or a false bottom in that coffin?"

"My name is Alucard," declared the Count, proudly drawing his thin frame up to its full height. "I am *Count* Alucard. I come from a noble Transylvanian family which stretches back across the centuries. A sliding panel? A false bottom? Believe me, sir, I would not so much as countenance either one of those subterfuges inside *my* coffin."

"So *you* say," replied Hargreaves from behind his counter. "But how am I to know whether you are telling me the truth or whether it's a whopping great fib?"

"Because I am a man of my word," said the Count. "Examine that coffin to your heart's content – you will find nothing untoward." Then,

taking hold of his cloak on either side with both of his hands, he spread them wide on either side of his body. "You have all of my possessions in front of you," he said. "But search me too if you don't believe me."

"I'm sure that won't be necessary," mumbled the Customs officer.

The truth of the matter was, of course, that Hilton Hargreaves was unable to step out from behind his counter. To have done so would have been to reveal the fact that, although the upper part of his body was smartly clothed in his Customs officer's uniform, his feet were contained in the panda slippers.

"I'm staying exactly where I am," the Customs

24

man continued to the Count. There was no way that he was going to display Aunt Edith's slippers to a member of the general public.

To tell the honest truth, Hilton Hargreaves was beginning to feel just a little bit ashamed of himself for the bad-tempered way he had treated the passenger. After all, the Customs officer admitted to himself, it wasn't a *crime* to use a coffin as a suitcase – it was just a little unusual, that was all.

"I'll tell you what, sir," said Hilton Hargreaves, picking up the Count's passport. "If your travel documents are in order, you can push off with the coffin and we'll say no more about it."

"Why, thank you," said the Count, delighted that his ordeal was almost over.

As the Customs officer flicked through the Transylvanian passport with its impressive gold-embossed double-headed eagle's insignia, the Count loaded his clothing back inside the coffin and put his other bits and pieces in his pockets.

"I'd say that's okey-dokey, sir," said Officer Hargreaves, handing back the passport with a smile.

"Thanks very much – I am indebted to you," said Count Alucard as he heaved his coffin back onto the trolley.

"Have a nice day!" called Hilton Hargreaves as the Count moved off, trundling the trolley towards the airport lounge.

Seconds later, after the Count had been swallowed up in the waiting throng, the Customs officer started to have second thoughts. A sixth sense began to tell him that there had been something slightly dodgy about the black-cloaked traveller, if only he could put his finger on it. . . The Customs officer tugged at the lobe of his left ear – a sign that he was thinking hard – and pondered over the several minutes he had spent questioning the man? "What was his name again?" Hargreaves asked himself. "Something beginning with 'A'. . . Allanby . . .? Atkinson . . .? Abercrombie . . .? No." And then, all at once, it came to him. "Alucard!" Yes, that was it! "*Count* Alucard!"

All at once, the Customs officer felt the short hairs on the back of his neck bristle against the inside of his uniform shirt-collar. He sucked in his breath and then let it out again in a long, low whistle. The awful truth had struck him, hard. 'ALUCARD' was 'DRACULA' backwards! And suddenly everything seemed to fall into place! Everything from why the man had carried his belongings in a coffin down to why he went around in a frilly white shirt, a black bow tie, a posh black suit and a crimson-lined black cloak. And – yes! – now that he came to think of it, the man had two pointy vampire teeth, one on either side of his mouth!

As if all of that was not proof enough, Hilton Hargreaves suddenly remembered that Count Alucard had handed him a Transylvanian passport. All vampires came from Transylvania. Hargreaves knew that for a certain fact.

With shaking hands, Hilton Hargreaves flicked through the pages of the Undesirable Visitors file. He turned to the page which contained, in alphabetical order, the names of all those frightening people which began with a 'D'. He ran his forefinger down the list:

DALEKS
DEADLY POISONOUS SNAKES
DOCTOR CRIPPEN (Deceased)
DOCTOR FRANKENSTEIN
DOCTOR FRANKENSTEIN'S MONSTER
DRACULA (Count) . . .

The Customs officer's forefinger began to shake more than ever. What was worse, beside the name there was an added entry in pencil: 'Not to be granted entry into the United Kingdom *under any circumstances* whatsoever. Signed: J.P. Cazelot, Chief Customs Officer.'

"Oh, crumbs!" murmured Hargreaves to himself. "Now I am in real hot water!"

The Customs officer gulped twice and swallowed hard. He had allowed a blood-drinking monster to enter England's green and pleasant land. No baby would be safe in its pram. No old lady could sleep easy in her bed. And he would lose his job, without a doubt . . .Or would he? Only a couple of minutes had elapsed since the cunning vampire count had tricked his way past him. There was still time to pursue and apprehend the villain. After all, had he not come a close third, only last year, in the 80 metres dash at the annual UK Customs Officers' Sports Day?

Hilton Hargreaves stooped behind his counter and assumed the position of an athlete in the starting-blocks. He murmured softly under his breath: "One to be ready, two to be steady—"

Before he could complete the phrase however, and launch himself in hot pursuit, his eyes caught sight of his feet. "Oh, blimey O'Reilly!" he muttered to himself.

What sort of a prize fool was he going to make of himself, chasing a blood-drinking vampire through the airport's busy outer lounge, wearing a pair of furry panda-faced slippers?

But the resourceful young Customs man was not beaten yet. Oh no, not by any means. He had a trick left up his sleeve. Reaching into his top pocket, he pulled out his Customs officer's whistle and let out three short, sharp piercing blasts.

"It's Dracula, lads!" cried Hilton Hargreaves as his fellow officers arrived on the scene. "I saw him with my own two eyes – with his long black hair and his pointy teeth!" Then, with a broad sweep of his arm in the direction of the lounge beyond, he added: "He went through there! Get after him!"

But, oddly enough, the two newcomers did not seem in a rush to tangle with the vampire count. They remained where they were, exchanging anxious glances and shuffling their feet.

"Do you mean *Count* Dracula?" asked the first.

"*Yes!*"

"*The* Count Dracula?" enquired the second. "The scary one that goes flying round at dead of night, biting people's necks and drinking all their blood?" he added with a shiver.

"*Yes!* Go chase him – quick!" urged Officer Hargreaves.

But neither of the other two officers seemed in any particular hurry to take up the vampire's

28

pursuit.

"Are you absolutely positive it *was* Dracula?" asked the first, adding: "What exactly did he look like?"

"I've told you!" snapped Hargreaves. "He's deathly white with red-rimmed eyes, pointy teeth and long black hair. He's wearing a posh black suit, a white frilly shirt, a black bow tie and a long black cloak with a crimson lining. Oh, yes – and he's got a gold medallion dangling round his neck. He looks just like he does in the late-night horror films on the telly."

"Spooky! It does *sound* like him," admitted the first officer. His name was Steven Wilkins. He had a bald head, a black moustache, and his hobby was keeping tropical fish. "On the other hand," he added, "it could be somebody dressed up to look like him."

"Don't be daft!" snapped Hilton Hargreaves. "Why would anyone want to dress up like Dracula to come through Customs?"

"They might – if they were going to a fancy dress party," said the second officer. His name was Ronnie Fairhurst. He was short, stout and had eyes that blinked continuously behind his gold-rimmed glasses. His hobby was doing jigsaw puzzles.

"It *is* him, I tell you!" snorted Hargreaves, angrily. "I've seen his passport. He comes from Transylvania – that's where all vampires come from. He calls himself Count Alucard – that's Dracula spelled backwards. I knew there was something odd about him the moment I saw him wheeling his coffin on an airport trolley—

29

"A *coffin*!" broke in Steven Wilkins, fearfully.

"Wow-*eee*!" mumbled Ronnie Fairhurst, blinking very fast.

"Look here," said Hargreaves sternly, "are you two going to go after him, or not? I wouldn't want to be in either of you two's shoes, when Chief Customs Officer Cazelot gets to hear that you've let Count Dracula slip through your fingers."

The smiles faded from the faces of both Wilkins and Fairhurst at the mention of their dreaded superior officer's name.

"Come *on*, Ronnie!" cried Steven Wilkins, assuming the role of leader and nervously pointing towards the busy lounge beyond. "Let's go get that vampire!"

With which brave cry, Stevie Wilkins led his fellow officer in pursuit of the evil blood-crazed monster which, they secretly and separately hoped, would be nowhere to be found.

3

"He went that way!"

The two Customs men bumped into each other as they tried to pull up sharply, the soles of their well-polished uniform black shoes skidding across the equally well-polished floor of the airport lounge. The lady who had spoken was wearing a floppy T-shirt bearing the picture of a colourful parrot.

"I beg your pardon, madam?" said Ronnie Fairhurst, breathlessly.

"That way!" snapped the lady, pointing across towards the exit. "If you hurry you might still catch him."

"Excuse me, madam," said Officer Wilkins, regaining his balance and raising his hat politely. "But just how exactly do *you* know who we're looking for?"

"Of course I know who you are looking for," replied the lady. "You're looking for Count Dracula. And I know which way he went, as I keep trying to tell you – through there!" Although several minutes had gone by since she had last set eyes on Count Alucard, Sylvia Cresswell's hand was still shaking as she pointed across the lounge towards the automatic plate-glass exit doors.

"And how do you know it *was* Count Dracula?" asked Customs Officer Wilkins, taking out his ballpoint pen and notebook as he wasted even more time. "It might have been someone dressed up to look like him."

As Stevie Wilkins continued to question the passenger, Ronnie Fairhurst allowed his glance to stray around the busy arrivals lounge. Everything *seemed* as normal to the Customs officer's well-trained eyes. There was the usual buzz of conversation as returning holiday-makers chattered excitedly to their relatives and friends there to meet and greet them. There was no sign, thank goodness, of anyone looking the least bit like a blood-sucking monster. *Good*! Customs Officer Fairhurst allowed himself to relax a little.

"I hope I know a vampire when I see one!" snapped Sylvia Cresswell, in answer to Wilkins' question. "Especially when I have stood as close to one as I am standing now to you – not once, but three times!"

"*Three* times?" repeated Wilkins, raising his eyebrows.

"I didn't just see him in here," said Mrs Cresswell proudly. "This one was my third time today."

"Well I never!" said Stevie Wilkins.

"Crikey Moses!" gasped Ronnie Fairhurst.

"First off, on the aeroplane, number two while I was waiting to collect my luggage," Sylvia Cresswell ticked off her vampire encounters on her fingers as she nodded down at the two bulging suitcases at her feet, and then continued: "and then this last time while I was standing here waiting for my husband to arrive. He's pushing a coffin on a trolley."

"Your husband is?" asked Ronnie Fairhurst who had not really been paying much attention. "So's the vampire."

"I'm *talking* about the vampire. I knew the minute I clapped eyes on him just who he was – with his pointy teeth, his long black cloak and his red-rimmed eyes." Sylvia Cresswell gave a little shiver.

Customs Officer Wilkins felt a little tingle of excitement run up his spine. This was good stuff! *Three* positive sightings! They had found a very important eye-witness. And even if they failed to catch the vampire, they would not return entirely empty-handed – they would have an eye-witness account to hand over to their superior officer. It would be proof to Chief Customs Officer Cazelot that they had not been shirking their job – at least, Steven Wilkins hoped it would. . .

"This is Customs Officer Fairhurst, madam," said Wilkins, handing Fairhurst his notebook and his ballpoint-pen. "He will take down your statement while I continue the search. I believe you stated that the monster made his exit by way of those plate-glass doors?"

"Yes – but I shouldn't think it'll do much good your going after him now." Mrs Cresswell gave a little sniff. "He's probably miles away – you've wasted too much time just standing about and talking."

"I think I am best qualified to be the judge of that, madam," said Wilkins in his official Customs officer's voice – but in his heart he hoped that what she said would prove to be the truth.

"Now, madam," began Officer Fairhurst, after Wilkins had set off towards the exit, "if we might begin with your name and address?"

Mrs Cresswell smiled a little smile that suggested she was keeping a secret to herself. "My goodness me," she said, "but you wouldn't make a very good detective, would you, Ronnie?"

"How do you know my first name?" asked the puzzled officer, blinking rapidly.

"I know a great deal more than that, Ronnie." Her smile had broadened into a grin. "I can tell you where you live as well."

"Go on then," said Ronnie Fairhurst, disbelievingly.

"No. 33, Reynard Avenue, off Coal Pit Lane, on that new estate."

"Golly Moses!" murmured the Customs man. "How the flip did you know that?"

"You'd be surprised at what I know and what I don't know, Ronnie Fairhurst," said Sylvia Cresswell with a chuckle. "Supposing I was to tell you that you've got a blue three-piece suite in your living-room; that the carpet's blue with red squiggles on it; and that there's a table-lamp on top of your telly shaped like a clown holding a yellow balloon up in the air."

There were several moments of silence. Customs Officer Fairhurst was at a total loss for words. Then, finding his tongue at last, he said: "Go on, you've got me up a gum-tree. Are you a fortune-teller or a mind-reader or something? I give up – tell me how you do it?"

"Easy-peasy," said Mrs Cresswell. "You *still* haven't worked out who I am, have you?"

Ronnie Fairhurst blinked hard, stared at the sun-burned face beneath the big straw hat, and slowly shook his head. "Now that you come to mention it, your face does ring a bell – but I'm afraid I can't quite. . ."

Sylvia Cresswell threw back her head and shook with laughter. The parrot on her T-shirt rose and fell as her shoulders went up and down. "Oh, very well," she said when she had caught her breath. "I'll put you out of your misery. I'm Mrs Cresswell. I'm married to Arthur Cresswell, the secretary of the Jigsaw Puzzler's Club."

"Of course you are!" Ronnie Fairhurst slapped the palm of his hand against his forehead. "You're Arthur's wife! Now I recognise you!"

"I should hope you do," said Sylvia Cresswell. "You *ought* to. The number of times I've popped round to your house on a Friday evening to bring you your fortnightly jigsaw puzzle – only you were always far too busy looking at the picture on the front of the box to pay any attention to who had brought it for you."

"Sorry," said Ronnie Fairhurst with a shamefaced smile and an apologetic shrug of his shoulders.

"Oh, that's all right," replied Sylvia Cresswell, not at all put out. "It's just the same at our house. When Arthur's got his head stuck over a jigsaw

puzzle, there's no getting through to him. Why, you could drop a bomb in our front garden and he wouldn't notice. I'll bet the reason I'm stuck here now, waiting for him to put in an appearance, is because he's sitting at the table, trying to finish off Christopher Columbus Sets Sail before he comes to pick me up."

"Did someone mention my name?" a voice asked, breezily. Arthur Cresswell, who had arrived unnoticed, was a tall man with a hooked nose and spiky hair that stuck out in all directions. He was wearing a shabby raincoat that seemed much too large for him. "Sorry I'm late, my love, but the traffic's been horrendous," he went on, giving his wife a quick peck on the cheek. Then, without giving her a chance to speak, he turned to the

Customs officer. "Well, well, well – this is an unexpected pleasure, Ronnie, bumping into you. How goes it with Windsor Castle? Have you managed to crack it yet?"

"Not quite, Arthur," the Customs man was forced to admit as he fingered a bit of jigsaw puzzle in his trouser pocket.

Ronnie Fairhurst had had Windsor Castle out on loan from the Jigsaw Puzzle Club for over a month – two weeks longer than he was supposed to keep it. But it had not been an easy puzzle to do. Admittedly, there were only 1000 pieces, but so many of them looked so alike. There was so much ivy-covered stonework. And then there had been that awful afternoon when, with the puzzle half-completed, Hilton Hargreaves had blundered into the rest-room, knocking the table over and sending 1000 jigsaw puzzle pieces skidding across the floor.

Fairhurst had spent an hour on his hands and knees, groping about underneath the lockers and the sofa, making absolutely sure every single bit was returned to the box. And then he had been faced with the awesome task of starting Windsor Castle all over again. It had not been his fault – but he could hardly tell the secretary that he was in the habit of taking the club's jigsaw puzzles to work. The club's rule book specifically stated that members were not to let the puzzles stray from the safety of their homes.

"If you'll excuse me, Arthur," said Ronnie Fairhurst hastily, deciding to put an end to the conversation. "See you tomorrow. Duty calls."

With which, and with a brief parting nod to Mrs Cresswell, he turned and hurried off in the direction of the plate-glass exit doors. "There seems to be a vampire roaming round the airport!" he called back over his shoulder.

"I must say, I did think he might have finished Windsor Castle by now," said Arthur Cresswell, ignoring the Customs officer's last words. "He's had it on loan for over a month. I wouldn't care, but he's got the brand new Balmoral out as well. He's keeping it out of circulation from the other members."

"Windsor Castle *is* hard, Arthur," said Sylvia Cresswell. "I seem to remember that even you had quite a job to finish it. It's the same with all that Famous Castles series – they've all got ever such a lot of ivy-covered stonework."

"There's ever such a lot of blue-green sea bits to Christopher Columbus Sets Sail," said Arthur Cresswell proudly. "But I didn't allow them to present me with a problem."

"You haven't, Arthur . . .!" gasped Mrs Cresswell " . . .You haven't finished Christopher Columbus?"

"I have."

"But it's got 1500 pieces."

"You don't need to tell me that, Sylvia," said her husband with a grin. "I've been eating my meals off a tray all week – Columbus only just fits on the dining-room table. Come on, Sylvia – let's hit the road. If I get my foot down, we can be home in half an hour and you'll be able to see the masterpiece in all its glory – before I put it back inside its box."

"But you've only just finished it, Arthur. Can't it stop where it is for a day or two – so we can look at it at our leisure?"

"No can do, Sylvia." Arthur Cresswell shook his head firmly. "I need the table." He stooped, picked up a suitcase in either hand, cleared his throat importantly and then made an announcement. "I'm going to tackle Captain Scott At The South Pole next," he said, then added: "It's another 1500-piecer in the Famous Explorers series."

"My goodness gracious, Arthur!" exclaimed Mrs Cresswell. "That'll be a hard nut to crack. Think of all the *snow* there'll be to fit in."

"I'll manage," said the jigsaw puzzle expert, comfortably.

"I don't know how you can even dare think of starting it."

"He who dares, wins," said Arthur Cresswell with a modest little shrug of his shoulders inside his shabby raincoat. "By the by," he added as they set off towards the door which led to the airport's car-park, "how was your holiday?"

"Well may you ask," said Sylvia, pulling a face. "First the hotel was only half-finished and there were all these workmen banging and hammering all day long, creating dust; *then* the pump had got clogged up so we couldn't use the swimming-pool; *then* it poured with rain last Wednesday but they wouldn't let us in the lounge because they had this wedding on; *then* they would insist on serving up *paella* every night for dinner – and nobody liked *paella*."

"It sounds as if you'd have been better off with

a week at Blackpool."

There were several moments of silence between them, broken only by the sound of Mrs Cresswell's flip-flops slapping urgently on the floor as she strove to keep up with her husband's loping strides. "If you ask me," she said at last, "I'd have been better off stopping at home and watching you. Fancy finishing Christopher Columbus Sets Sail in seven days! You stagger me sometimes, Arthur. You are a wonder!"

The secretary of the northern branch of the Jigsaw Puzzlers Club glanced down fondly at his wife. Sylvia Cresswell returned the glance and gave her husband a happy smile. His interesting news on the jigsaw puzzle front had made her quite forget her several creepy encounters with the vampire.

4

"Do you mean to say that you've got the bare-faced cheek to stand there and tell me that you didn't get that eye-witness's statement?" said Steven Wilkins, glowering angrily at Ronnie Fairhurst.

"Sorry, Steve," Fairhurst mumbled, not daring to look his fellow officer in the eye.

"Why not? What were you thinking of?"

Ronnie Fairhurst shook his head, kept his eyes on the ground, but said nothing. How could he explain that, what with the initial surprise of the eye-witness turning out to be the jigsaw puzzle club's secretary's wife – and then with the added excitement of the jigsaw puzzle club secretary turning up in person – the task which Wilkins had asked him to perform had totally slipped his mind. "What about the vampire?" he asked, changing the subject and glancing round the airport's forecourt. "Any sign of him with his coffin, spooking about and doing his stuff?"

Customs Officer Wilkins shook his head. "Not so much as a sniff of him," he said forlornly. It really was too bad of Fairhurst. No vampire's apprehension to report and now no signed statment

41

of the eye-witness's triple sighting to take back to Chief Customs Officer Cazelot. Their superior officer would go potty! He would go raving mad! "You've really landed us in bother, Ronnie," said Wilkins. "I hope you know that."

"I've said I'm sorry, Stevie. What more can I do?" replied Fairhurst, sticking his hands down deep in his trouser-pockets and taking a kick at a discarded squashed empty can. The can flew through the air, hit the ground, rattled noisily across the concrete and finally came to rest as it clattered up against a litter-bin marked 'KEEP THIS AIRPORT TIDY'. "Goal!" yelled Customs Officer Fairhurst, throwing his hands up in the air.

"Belt up, Ronnie!" growled Steven Wilkins. He frowned as he glanced around the airport forecourt in a last half-hearted attempt at spotting either the dreaded vampire or its sinister coffin.

Wilkins observed the line of waiting taxis which moved up, one by one, to accommodate the steady stream of returning holidaymakers, pushing their loaded trolleys.

Some of these tourists, having been to Spain, were wearing large Spanish souvenir sombreros or carrying castanets; others, who had been holidaying in Florida sunshine, were sporting Disney World souvenir Mickey Mouse ears; while others, who had been cruising on the Nile, had Egyptian souvenir fezzes on their heads or large stuffed souvenir toy camels balanced on top of their luggage trolleys. But there was no sign whatsoever of the black-cloaked, pointy-toothed vampire trundling his spooky coffin . . .

"Come on then, Ronaldo, me laddo," Wilkins began reluctantly. "We might as well get it over with – we'll go and see the chief and tell him we've drawn a blank."

"He'll go raving bonkers," gulped Customs Officer Fairhurst blinking rapidly.

"I know," groaned Customs Officer Wilkins. "He'll go round the flipping twist."

"Whereabouts in the city did you say you wanted dropping, chum?" said the taxi-driver as he glanced into his rear-mirror at the strangely-dressed passenger huddled on the back seat of his cab.

"A very good question," said Count Alucard softly to himself. In fact, when he had hired the cab outside the airport terminal, he had not given the driver any specific destination – for the sole and simple reason that he did not know himself where he wanted to be taken.

One of the most vexing things about being born a vampire, as the Count had discovered many years before, was this inability to plan one's travelling arrangements in advance. Although he had led an entirely blameless life and never done anything that he was in any way ashamed of, because he had been born into a noble vampire family, Count Alucard seemed to spend a great deal of his time either evading hot-tempered policemen who sought to lock him up, or running away from angry villagers who seemed to want to slice him into little pieces with gleaming scythes or to puncture his person with sharp-pronged pitchforks.

For these reasons then, Count Alucard deemed it best not to make any arrangements too far ahead, for fear that such plans might be found out by those who sought to kill or capture him. If he wished to pack his coffin with clean clothes and go off in search of happier times, he made that decision on the morning of the day of his departure. He looked to find lodgings where he might lay his head when he arrived at his destination and not before. It was not the ideal way of life for an international traveller, but at least it served to keep him alive and in one piece . . .

"I said: 'Whereabouts would you like me to drop you off, chief?' " repeated the taxi-driver, again glancing into his rear-view mirror as he steered his cab through the increasing traffic which indicated that they were approaching the centre of the northern city.

"My dear good fellow, I am in your kind hands entirely," said Count Alucard, apologetically. He had decided that he could do no better than tell the truth. "To be absolutely honest with you," he continued, "I desire food and lodging but I have no idea whatsoever as to where my needs might best be served?"

"Well now, what exactly are you looking for?" asked the taxi-driver, more than willing to help his passenger in any way that he could. "A posh four-star hotel with all the trimmings? Or would a humble bed-and-breakfast boarding house, offering cosy home comforts, be more to your liking?"

"I think a *big* hotel would suit the best—" began

the Count who knew, from past experience, that his curious presence would occasion the least excitement in a large establishment. He could lose himself in the vast lounges and long corridors of a big hotel. In a small boarding-house, on the other hand, the proprietor could hardly fail to be inquisitive about his manner of dress – or to object when his coffin took up most of the room in a small front parlour.

But before Count Alucard could finish what he had begun to say, he became aware of a police car's screaming siren. The urgent sounds were somewhere in the distance, thankfully, but were growing louder with each passing second. There could be little doubt that he was the person that the police car's occupants were out to apprehend.

There could be small doubt either that it would not take long for them to track him down – considering that his coffin was perched on the luggage rack on the taxi's roof! It was essential that they turn off the main road into the city immediately. And that the taxi should shake off the following police car in some quiet backwater.

"—As I was saying, a *big* hotel would probably suit me best," the Count began again. "But preferably one that is set in the countryside and not the city centre – I *do* so like to wake up to the sound of chirruping bird-song in the morning."

"Leave it to me, chiefy," said the obliging taxi-driver. "I know the very place that will suit you down to the ground." With which, he swung the steering-wheel and the taxi turned off the main road and into a less busy thoroughfare. Within seconds, they had left the city traffic behind them and were heading into the tree-lined suburbs.

More important though, as far as Count Alucard was concerned, the police car's siren had faded into the distance.

The taxi-driver, whose name was Monty Wilson, began to whistle a cheerful tune. He was completely unaware that his cab had been the target of a police car's attentions. Neither had it so much as crossed his mind that the oddly-attired passenger in the back of his cab was, in fact, a vampire count. Had he been aware of both – or even either – of these facts, Monty Wilson would not have whistled quite so merry a tune.

But Monty's mind was on other matters. Today was Friday. Tomorrow, all things being equal,

46

would be Saturday. The weekend, with all of its attendant delights, loomed large in Monty Wilson's thoughts. The taxi-driver kept his work to a minimum at the weekend. Saturdays and Sundays, as far as Monty was concerned, were for more important things.

Monty Wilson's hobby (his obsession, according to Maisie, his long-suffering wife) was collecting antique corkscrews. The Wilsons' semi-detached home was awash with antique corkscrews. There were antique corkscrews on display in cabinets in the sitting-room; there were antique corkscrews tastefully arranged in rows above the telephone table in the hall; there was a rash of antique corkscrews hanging on the wall and leading from the foot of the stairs to the first floor landing.

On most Saturday mornings, Monty's cab sat idly in the garage while its owner scoured the northern junk-shops for antique corkscrews to add to his collection. His Sundays were spent at car-boot sales but with the very same object in view. Even when the Wilsons went on holiday, while their lucky fellow tourists swam in the warm blue waters of the Mediterranean, or played bingo in the cool air-conditioning of their hotel lounge, Maisie found herself being hustled around smelly, blue-bottle buzzing flea-markets in the never-ending search for antique corkscrews.

Monty Wilson's thoughts had been on corkscrews when he had helped his passenger to load the coffin onto the taxi's roof-rack. He had also been day-dreaming about corkscrews when the police car's siren had sounded at his rear. And he was considering corkscrews now, and wondering what the morrow might bring, as he steered the taxi away from the city's centre, whistling his sprightly tune.

The taxi-driver's tuneful whistling served to cheer up the Count who snuggled down in his seat and sighed, contentedly, as he gazed out of the window at the passing show of suburban tree-lined avenues.

Chief Customs Officer Granville Cazelot removed his gaze from the framed photograph of the German Shepherd dog hanging on his office wall and smiled, pleasantly, at the three officers who were paraded in front of him.

"Well then!" said the chief officer as he arranged his pen, pencil, ruler and eraser in a neat row on the spotless square of blotting-paper which the cleaner had put in his blotting-pad that morning. "I sincerely hope that you three men are entirely satisfied with your day's work?" he continued, the smile spreading across his face.

Customs Officers Hilton Hargreaves, Steven Wilkins and Ronnie Fairhurst shifted their feet uneasily on the square of carpet in front of their boss's desk.

The very fact that Chief Officer Cazelot had spoken pleasantly and smiled at them was a sure sign that he was hopping mad. Granville Cazelot was rarely pleasant and seldom smiled except when something or someone had got up his nostrils – and then, when he turned his smile on his luckless

48

victim, it had the same strange hypnotic effect as a roused cobra's piercing stare. And, as with a cobra, when Chief Cazelot smiled, you needed to look into his eyes if you wanted to know the real way that he was feeling. Customs officers throughout the length and breadth of the north of England would rather have faced an entire gang of well-armed smugglers than stand in front of Chief Customs Officer Cazelot when he wore a smile on his face.

The three officers who were suffering that doubtful privilege cleared their throats, nervously and in unison.

If anything, Hilton Hargreaves's throat-clearing sounded just a tidge more nervously high-pitched than the clearing sounds that came out of the throats of his fellow officers. This was understandable. On top of his failure to stop the undesirable alien vampire from entering the United Kingdom, Customs Officer Hilton Hargreaves was also improperly dressed. He was still wearing his Aunt Edith's birthday gift panda slippers. He had suffered more than his fair share of snide remarks and sniggerings from Stevie Wilkins and Ronnie Fairhurst while they waited outside Chief Cazelot's office.

For the moment, though, so long as the Head of Customs remained sitting behind his desk, the slippers were hidden from his view. But the young Customs officer knew full well that, should the chief rise and cross the office, the two impish panda faces would be instantly in his eyeline. Hilton Hargreaves offered up a silent prayer for his superior officer to stay where he was.

"You don't deserve to be in the Customs Service – not one of you!" snapped Granville Cazelot, rising and crossing around his desk.

"Thanks for nothing, God!" murmured Hilton Hargreaves as he closed his eyes, crossed his fingers, wished that the earth might open and swallow him up – and waited for the worst to happen. He heard Chief Cazelot's heavy footsteps crossing the office, then there was silence for what seemed an age – an age in which Hilton Hargreaves' life seemed to pass in front of his tightly-closed eyes . . .

"If I had my way," Chief Customs Officer Cazelot's voice finally broke in on Hilton Hargreaves' vivid images of his childhood, which had moved on from his baby-buggy days to a carefree holiday he had once enjoyed as an eleven-year-old at Scarborough, "you'd be booted out of the Customs Service dishonourably, and transferred to mopping out the airport's lavatories – all three of you!"

"All *three*?" Hilton Hargreaves opened his eyes and blinked with relief as he realised that he was not being singled out for criticism. Chief Cazelot had not seen his slippers. He had crossed the office, it seemed, without once glancing down towards the floor, his eyes fixed firmly on the German Shepherd dog's photograph on the wall.

"In fact, if I had my way," Granville Cazelot began again, "I wouldn't have you hopeless helpless incompetents under my command at all." He paused, rubbed his hands together gleefully, and then added: "Do you want to know what I'd have instead?"

"A Customs service manned by Alsatian dogs, chief?" said Hilton Hargreaves, helpfully.

"They're not *Alsatian* dogs, Hargreaves!" snapped the chief officer, still gazing proudly at the photograph. "Let's give them their proper name, shall we, if we're going to refer to them – they're called German Shepherd dogs, by those of us in the know. And do you know *why* I'd rather have German Shepherd dogs serving under me than you lot?"

"Because they can run faster than we can, chief?" suggested Fairhurst, adding: "And the drug-dealers and other suchlike undesirables would be more scared of them than they are of us?"

"They'd be good at sniffing out drugs too, chief," proffered Steven Wilkins.

"And they're more obedient than humans," added Hilton Hargreaves.

The three customs officers had been forced to listen to Chief Cazelot's dreams of a Customs service staffed entirely by himself and German Shepherd dogs so many times that they knew all of his reasons for such a scheme off by heart. But Cazelot reacted as though he had never so much as mentioned the idea before.

"Very good – very good indeed!" he announced. He lifted the framed photograph off the wall, carefully, and carried it back with him behind his desk, before continuing: "And do you know which German Shepherd dog I'd have in charge of all the rest?"

51

"Wolf, chief!" said Hargreaves, Fairhurst and Wilkins, in unison.

"*Cor*—rect!" snapped the chief.

Wolf, the German Shepherd dog pictured in the photograph, was Granville Cazelot's pride and joy. When the Customs man left for work in the mornings, his very last action was to give the dog a friendly pat over the garden gate. When he came back home in the evenings, after a hard day at the airport, it was Wolf again that Granville Cazelot sought out first. "I sometimes think, Granville," Clara Cazelot, the Customs officer's wife, had been known to remark, "that you care more about that dog than you do about me." And Granville Cazelot always laughed when Clara proffered the preposterous remark – but he had never been known to deny the suggestion.

Every Saturday, Granville Cazelot entered the dog in several categories at some local show or other where, over the several years that he had owned him, Wolf had won six first prize rosettes for Best of Breed, eight first prize rosettes for Obedience and, on one never-to-be-forgotten occasion, had been awarded a small, silver-plated cup which the proud Customs officer had had suitably engraved:

WOLF
Best Dog in Show
Owner
G. CAZELOT Esq.

Every Sunday morning, on the Cazelots' well-trimmed lawn, the Customs man put Wolf through his show routines. While Clara watched through the kitchen window as she peeled potatoes or polished the Best Dog in Show trophy, Wolf rolled over on command, or pretended to lie dead, or dutifully obeyed such orders as "Heel!", "Stay!" and "Here, boy!"

"You've made a right dog's dinner out of this morning's work," sneered Chief Customs Officer Cazelot. He was still holding up Wolf's photograph and his eyes narrowed as they took in the officers who were standing to attention in front of him. "Because I'll tell you this for nothing – if my Wolfie had been on duty at the desk this morning, he wouldn't have let a vampire sneak past him."

Wilkins, Fairhurst and Hargreaves, not daring to look their superior officer in the eye, hung their heads and stood in shamefaced silence.

"You can thank your lucky stars, all three of you, that I managed to get Police Inspector Archie

Oliver on the phone. That vampire won't get far with his coffin with Inspector Oliver on his tail." Granville Cazelot paused, and then continued sourly: "The only fly in the ointment being that if Archibald *does* nick the vampire, it'll be him that gets the credit and not yours truly. Get out of here! And get back on duty before I do something to you that I might have cause to regret!"

As Cazelot's door closed behind them, Wilkins, Fairhurst and Hargreaves sighed with relief. All things considered, they had got off very lightly – extremely lightly indeed.

"I don't suppose," began Ronnie Fairhurst, blinking hopefully through his glasses, "that either of you two fancy putting in half an hour on Windsor Castle?" He dug a hand in his trouser pocket, took out the bit of jigsaw and held it up for the others to see. "Only I've found that corner piece that we thought had gone missing."

"Sorry, Ronaldo," said Steven Wilkins, shaking his head and thinking about the tropical fish firm's catalogue that was in his raincoat pocket. "I'm afraid I've got other things to do . . ."

"You'll have to count me out too, Ronnie," said Hilton Hargreaves, casting a sly glance down at his feet and wiggling his toes self-consciously inside his slippers. "I must get back behind my desk."

The three Customs officers went their separate ways. Each of them seemed to move with a new, light-hearted spring in his step. All three had dismissed the incident of the vampire from their minds and replaced it with a more pleasing prospect.

It was Friday afternoon and the weekend loomed excitingly ahead. Tomorrow would be Saturday and they had important matters to attend to. One of them was looking forward keenly to an important meeting of the Jigsaw Puzzlers Club (Northern branch). A second one was eagerly anticipating the Annual General Meeting of the Aquarium Society. The third intended a visit to the city centre and a shopping mall where he was going to treat himself to a decent pair of slippers that didn't look back at him cross-eyed whenever he glanced down at them . . .

For these three separate reasons then, Ronnie Fairhurst, Steven Wilkins and Hilton Hargreaves were looking forward to the next day's coming – they might not have relished its arrival quite so much, perhaps, had they been aware that, before the next day was over, they would have their mettles tested in another spooky encounter with the coffin-carrying vampire count.

5

Chief Customs Officer Cazelot chewed angrily at his lower lip as he returned Wolf's photograph to its place on his office wall. Unlike his junior officers, Granville Cazelot had *not* dismissed the vampire from his mind. It was not the first time, he reflected bitterly, that his men had let him down – but never before quite so seriously. This time, he told himself, they had gone too far. They had allowed an evil undesirable blood-drinking monster to enter the United Kingdom. There was nothing now that he could do about it. The matter was out of his hands. The fate of every man, woman and child in the country depended now upon the skill and dedication of Police Inspector Archie Oliver.

Granville Cazelot had known Archie Oliver for a long, long time. The police inspector was a dog-lover like himself. The two men bumped into each other frequently on Saturday afternoons at dog shows across the length and breadth of the north of England.

Unlike the Customs officer though, the police inspector had little interest in German Shepherd dogs. Archie Oliver's dog was a snow-white French poodle called Trixiebelle the Third.

But the fact that the two men preferred different breeds of dogs was no hindrance to their friendship – if anything, it served to strengthen the relationship. It meant that they were seldom in competition with each other. If Wolf won first prize for Best of Breed in the German Shepherd dog class, then no-one was more delighted than Archie Oliver. Should Trixiebelle the Third be declared best French poodle at any show, then it was Granville Cazelot who led the congratulatory hand-clapping. And, when the competition was over, the two men sought out each other's company in the refreshment marquee where they both raised their glasses to each other's dog.

"Good luck, Archie," muttered Granville Cazelot softly to himself as he straightened Wolf's photograph on the office wall. He also told himself that if there was one policeman in the whole of England that could be counted upon to apprehend the monster, then that copper was Archie Oliver.

"Lost it?" groaned Police Inspector Oliver to the young policewoman driver who was guiding the police car through the main road's busy traffic. "What do you mean, you've 'lost it'?"

"Sorry, sir," replied Sandra Simmons as she did her best to peer through the mass of traffic up ahead. "I thought I spotted the target vehicle some minutes ago, headed towards the city centre – but it seems to have disappeared completely."

"Taxis don't just 'disappear', missie," growled the inspector. "Particularly when they've got a flippin' great shiny black coffin balanced on the roof. What you're trying to tell me is that whoever's driving that taxi has put his foot down, picked up speed and you can't drive fast enough to catch up with him?"

"No, sir," replied the young police constable, trying hard not to lose her temper. "What I'm trying to tell you is that I think that the taxi-driver may have turned off into one of the side streets some way back in an attempt to lose us."

"Oh, yes?" scoffed Archie Oliver. "He wouldn't have managed that, policewoman, if you'd kept your eyes peeled."

"No, and he wouldn't have got away, inspector, if you'd kept *your* eyes on the road ahead and not spent the last five minutes gloating over those French poodle photographs in your wallet," thought Sandra Simmons – but, wisely, she kept her feelings to herself. Instead, she said aloud: "Shall I turn back, inspector, and check out all the side turnings that we've passed?"

"I shouldn't bother," sniffed Archie Oliver. "That vampire'll be miles away by now – thanks to you. I'll tell you what you can do – you can drive me back to Central, double-smartish, so I can type out my report. No prizes for guessing who won't be coming out of that with any credit." He paused, then added gleefully: "But I'll give you a clue. She's got red hair, green eyes and a lot of freckles."

Policewoman Simmons did not need to glance into her rear-view mirror to know that she fitted the description exactly. Again she decided that she would be best advised to hold her tongue.

58

In the silence that followed, the inspector sneaked a glance at his wristwatch. In fact, he had no intention whatsoever of writing out a report that afternoon. He had it in his mind that tomorrow was Saturday. Trixiebelle the Third was entered into a dog show and Archie Oliver was anxious to get home as soon as possible. He wanted to give Trixibelle a nice shampoo before Mrs Oliver came home from doing the weekly shop and needed him to help her unpack.

"You heard me, Simmons," snapped the inspector. "Get your foot down, girl." He paused, then added a phrase which he had learned from his favourite American TV police series: "Burn rubber!"

"Here we are then, guv'nor," said Monty Wilson over his shoulder as he stopped outside the entrance to the hotel. "How does this suit?"

"My dear good fellow!" exclaimed Count Alucard, peering out of the taxi's window. "It is perfectly ideal! It is ideally perfect!"

The big hotel, which was called Laburnum Towers, was everything the Count had hoped for – and a great deal more. Set in its own expansive grounds, hidden from the road by trees, the sprawling several storeyed modern hotel was just the place where he might conveniently hide himself, in comfort, until the hue and cry, caused by his arrival in the United Kingdom, had died down.

Count Alucard guessed that the airport authorities had raised the alarm. Furthermore he knew from past experience that if one police car sought to take him into custody – and failed – it would not be very long before a whole fleet of similar vehicles were out looking for him.

"All things considered, my dear old thing," the Count murmured to himself, "you would be well advised to take your ease in this excellent establishment for a day or two and simply allow the world to pass you by—"

"And what do we have here?" said the hotel doorman stepping forward. As he did so, the Count took two steps backwards.

The hotel doorman was heavily built and sported a military moustache. He was wearing a pale blue uniform which was liberally decorated with gold braid and seemed to have more gold buttons than was needed. Count Alucard distrusted all men in uniform. While the general public were, for the most part, either inclined to acknowledge his presence with a nervous smile or even pretend that they hadn't seen him – when he encountered anyone in uniform then that person could usually be counted on to start asking questions. . . .

"Am I to take it that this coffin belongs to you?" said the hotel doorman, glancing up at the Count's sleek black casket which was still attached to the taxi's roof-rack.

"Er . . .well . . .you see . . .as it happens . . ." mumbled the Count, unhappily.

"Yes, Stanley, that is the gentleman's luggage," said Monty Wilson, who had got down from his cab.

"What ho, Monty, my old mate! I didn't see

you standing there," cried the hotel doorman. It seemed that the doorman and the taxi-driver were good friends. "If you'll give me a hand to get the gentleman's doings down," the doorman continued, "I'll summon the porters and have them wheel it indoors." Then, turning to the Count, he said: "You're not the first one of your ilk to get here, sir, not by any means. The first one arrived this morning, all the way from Cardiff—" the doorman paused, chuckled, then drew a forefinger across his throat, and went on: "—with a bloodstained guillotine in the back of his van – oh yes, and we had a gentleman turn up this afternoon with a sort of Chinese Torture Cabinet on the back of his trailer."

"What kind of a Chinese Torture Cabinet?" asked the Count, his eyes widening in surprise.

"You know the sort of thing," the doorman continued with a bloodthirsty chuckle. "You lock a chap inside it and then stick long sharp swords through all the sides."

Count Alucard's heart fluttered inside his chest at the very thought of such an awful torture happening to himself.

"There'll be all sorts of hi-jinks going on in Laburnum Towers this weekend then, Stanley?" said Monty Wilson gleefully and not at all disturbed, it seemed, at the cruelties the doorman had hinted at.

"It's not for me to reveal what kind of mumbo-jumbo this gentleman and his chums will be getting up to," replied the doorman, giving the Count a conspiratorial wink as he tapped the side of his nose with his forefinger. "But things will be happening in the old hotel, Montgomery – I should say so, yes indeedy!" As he spoke, the hotel doorman rubbed his hands together gleefully.

Count Alucard gulped, twice, but said nothing. He hadn't the faintest idea who the doorman had mistaken him for – or what manner of gruesome hi-jinks were scheduled to take place in the hotel. He only knew that he did not want any part of them. Blood-stained guillotines and sinister Chinese cabinets were hardly *his* cup of tea. On the other hand, he could hardly reveal his true identity and declare himself a Transylvanian vampire count.

For a moment, the Count wondered whether he should make some sort of excuse to the doorman and ask the taxi-driver to take him somewhere else? But already it was too late. Between them, the cabbie and the hotel doorman had manhandled his precious coffin down onto the gravel drive and a hotel porter was loading it onto a trolley.

"You'll enjoy it here, chiefy, you really will," Monty Wilson assured the Count who, with shaking hands, was taking out his wallet in order to pay his taxi-fare.

"This way, sir!" said the hotel doorman, beckoning the Count towards the hotel's entrance. With sinking heart, preceded by the porter pushing his coffin on a trolley, Count Alucard allowed Stanley Groves, the hotel doorman, to lead him into Laburnum Towers.

In the quiet of the garden shed, as the afternoon drifted into early evening, Henry Hollins studied the monogrammed address at the top of the mauve-coloured writing-paper and then read the letter from the vegetarian vampire for the umpteenth time.

Henry, my dear good friend,

It is that time of year again when the English Cox's Pippin apples are at their tip-top crunchiest best and plump mushrooms are there for early-morning taking in every dew-wet English meadow. For both of these reasons (and several others) I am planning another visit to your delightful country. Hoorah! I do not know, as yet, where I shall be staying or when, exactly, I shall arrive (except that it shall be sooner rather than later). But as soon as I am safely settled in, be sure that I shall look you up.

Looking forward tremendously to seeing you again and assuring you of my continuing friendship.

Warmest regards as always,
Count Alucard

" . . .*sooner rather than later* . . ." Henry Hollins repeated those four important words to himself as he carefully re-folded the letter, replaced it in the envelope and then returned it for safe-keeping to his pocket.

Letters posted in Tolokovin, the tiny village which nestled at the foot of Alucard Mountain, might sometimes take a week or even more to reach the United Kingdom. All mail from Tolokovin, as Henry well knew, travelled first by ox-cart for several days along a bumpy, winding forest path before reaching the main road leading to the nearest town. It was possible that Count Alucard might travel faster than his letter and could have arrived already?

One thing was certain, Henry told himself, it was important that he spend the next day or two inside the house and certainly stray no further than the garden, in case the Count telephoned or even presented himself at the Hollinses' front door in person. . .

"What would you say, Henry," began Albert Hollins, popping his head round the door of the

65

garden shed, "to a trip out, with your mum and me, in the car tomorrow?"

"No, thanks, Dad," said Henry, quickly. "But thanks all the same for asking."

"But you haven't heard yet about the surprise that I've got planned for you," protested Mr Hollins.

"I'll bet that it's going to be fantastic, Dad – your surprises always are – and I'm *really* sorry to say 'no', but I can't tomorrow."

"Oh?" said Mr Hollins suspiciously. "Why not?"

"Because I've got to go to school," lied Henry, crossing his fingers behind his back.

"But it's Saturday tomorrow – *and* it's the middle of the holidays."

"I know," said Henry, crossing the fingers on both of his hands at once. "But we're doing this project about vampires next term, Dad, and I promised Mr Grantley that I'd go in, during the holidays, and hang some plastic bats on thread from the form-room ceiling."

"Spooky!" said Mr Hollins.

"Yes," said Henry, adding: "By the way, what was it going to be?"

"What was what going to be?" asked Albert Hollins with a puzzled frown.

"The surprise you said you'd got planned for me?"

"Ah!" replied his father with a cunning smile. "If I told you that, young man, you'd be as wise as me. Besides, it wouldn't be a surprise then, would it?"

"But if there isn't going to be an outing, Dad,

66

be?"

"But there *is* going to be an outing, Henry. And you *are* going on it, believe you me. Most definitely. Your mum's gone down to the supermarket to get some stuff to put inside the sandwiches and so forth. We're going to stop off for a picnic en route to our secret destination. That much I am at liberty to tell you – but as far as that destination goes, my lips are sealed." And, as if to prove his point, Albert Hollins shut his lips tightly and pressed a forefinger against them.

"But what about my school project?"

"I'm afraid you'll have to postpone your bat-hanging activities until another day. You can ring Mr Grantley and rearrange things. I'm sure that *he* won't mind – and the bats, being made of plastic, won't give a hoot. Okey-dokey?"

"Okey-dokey," Henry Hollins echoed his father's words despondently. He knew that his father's mind was made up and that further argument would be a waste of time. Henry sighed and resigned himself to the fact that, if the Count should chance to ring or even call at the Hollins' house on the following day, there would be nobody in to pick up the phone or answer the doorbell.

"By the by, Henry," said Mr Hollins, closing the door of the garden shed and changing the subject. "You remember that card trick I was showing you and your mother earlier?"

"The one that didn't work?"

"That's not *quite* true, young man. *Most* of it worked – it was just the end bit that I hadn't quite

67

got off pat. Only I've been having another look at the instructions that came with it. . . ." As he spoke, Albert Hollins reached into his cardigan pocket, took out a single sheet of paper and, kneeling down, spread the printed instructions on the shed floor. " . . .I think I know where I've been going wrong," he said. Reaching into his other cardigan pocket, Mr Hollins again produced his pack of cards then, with one eye peering at the instructions and his other eye on the cards, he fanned the pack in front of Henry's face. "Take a card," he said. "Any card – it doesn't matter which."

"This one," said Henry, selecting a card without much enthusiasm.

"You're absolutely certain that's the one you want?"

"Positive," said Henry, glancing at the card which was the Seven of Spades.

"You're sure you don't want to change your mind? Because you are quite at liberty to do so – should that be your desire," said Mr Hollins in his best magician's voice.

"No, thanks."

"Very well." Mr Hollins again fanned the cards, face down. "Put your card back in the pack – anywhere you like. But don't let me see what it is." Henry did so. "Now then," continued Mr Hollins, "what was the number you were thinking of?"

"What number?" asked Henry.

"The number I asked you to think of before you chose the card."

"You didn't ask me to think of a number," said Henry.

"Didn't I?" Mr Hollins squinted at his page of printed instructions. "My mistake," he said. "I should have done. It says so here. Perhaps we'd better start the trick again." And Mr Hollins shuffled the cards once more, energetically but rather clumsily, and succeeded in dropping three cards on the floor.

Henry Hollins puffed out his cheeks and sucked in his breath with exasperation. It was turning into a *very* exasperating afternoon. A sixth sense told him that his friend, Count Alucard, the Transylvanian vegetarian vampire, *had* arrived in the United Kingdom. Was it possible, Henry wondered, that the Count was in some sort of trouble? If so, why hadn't he got in touch with Henry – and, more importantly, what could Henry do in order to contact the Count . . .?

"Choose a card," said Mr Hollins, spreading the pack yet again in front of Henry's face. "Hang on a tick! Don't choose a card – not yet – think of a number first, between ten and thirty."

"Oops-a-daisy!" said the hotel porter as he eased the shiny black coffin from off his porter's trolley and onto the bedroom floor. The porter – whose name was Kevin Protheroe – was a keen young man who believed that his job as hotel porter was the first exciting step up a ladder which would take him, eventually, to the highest rung and the post of hotel manager. "There you go, sir," he added, politely touching his porter's cap with his forefinger. "Will that be all that you'll be requiring?"

"That's absolutely splendid!" said the Count. Searching in his trouser pockets, he located a couple of coins and pressed them into Kevin Protheroe's hand, adding: "Thank you."

"Thank *you*, sir!" replied the porter, but his smile faded quickly into a frown. "Just a jiffy," he continued. "I can't get myself a fizzy drink with these – they're *foreign* coins."

"I do apologise," said the Count, spreading his hands wide, palms upturned and long, slim fingers outstretched. "They're Transylvanian grubecks. The taxi-driver took all my English change and those are all that I have left about my person. But do permit me to assure you, my dear chap that, should you ever go to Transylvania, those coins will purchase you a mug of fresh warm goat's milk or a slice of currant shrubel-cake from any farmhouse kitchen in the land."

Kevin Protheroe left the bedroom with a puzzled frown and scratching his head as he considered the unlikelihood of his ever being able to take up the Count's suggestion.

Count Alucard, alone at last and in his hotel bedroom, was also puzzled. Neither the girl receptionist, nor the hotel porter nor, for that matter, any of the hotel staff or guests that he had encountered on his way to his bedroom, had shown the slightest interest in the coffin on the porter's trolley. Indeed, one guest in the crowded lift – a short, fat man with a bald head and a briefcase – had been so unconcerned at the coffin's close proximity that he had drummed out a little tune

70

with his fingers on its side as they travelled up to the top floor.

It really *was* most disturbing, the Count decided as he lowered the coffin to the carpeted floor, opened the lid and started to unpack his things. First there had been the mysterious mention of the blood-stained guillotine and the sinister Chinese cabinet *and* the talk of 'hi-jinks' in Laburnum Towers over the coming weekend. And now this curious unconcern displayed by all about his coffin. *Most* unusual.

"This hotel would appear to be rampant with *very* weird folk this weekend," the vegetarian vampire count murmured to himself as he carefully arranged the items from his toilet-bag in a neat row along the bathroom shelf. "In fact, all things considered," he added, "I don't think that I shall venture out of my room this evening." Then, glancing into the mirror over the washbasin, he was saddened, if not surprised, to discover that he could see everything in the bathroom reflected in the glass – except himself.

In company with all vampires, Count Alucard did not possess a reflection. No matter where or when he looked into a mirror, the Count was never rewarded with the reassuring sight of his own image gazing back at him. It was a most unfortunate phenomenon. It meant that he was constantly nicking himself while shaving and, also, that he was unable to arrange a neat parting when he ran a comb through his long, black hair. But it was one of life's little bugbears that vampires have to learn to put up with.

When he was at home in Transylvania, the Count was hardly ever aware of the problem. His late father, the previous Count Alucard, had had the good sense to have every single mirror in Alucard Castle taken down. It was only at such times as these – when he was on his travels – that this lack of a reflection came to his notice.

Count Alucard sighed and gave a little shiver as he gazed gravely into the bathroom mirror. There was something rather disheartening, he always felt, about looking into a looking-glass and seeing nothing but an empty room. There was something saddening too, he sighed to himself, about spending an entire evening in a lonely hotel bedroom. . . .

But before an hour had passed, Count Alucard's natural good humour had dispelled the cloud of gloom. Dressed in his crimson silk monogrammed pyjamas, he was sitting up in the snug warmth of his coffin which, for added comfort, he had lifted up onto the bed. A bowl containing a scrumptious

avocado salad was balanced on his lap and an entire basket of delicious fresh fruit was within hand's reach – both of these items having arrived by courtesy of room-service and delivered by a friendly waitress called Connie Leatherbarrow.

To add to his enjoyment, the Count had the latest edition of his favourite magazine, *The Coffin-Makers' Journal*, to while away the hours. That month's copy was a particularly good one, too. The main feature, with several coloured illustrations, was about the very latest in luxury coffins manufactured in the USA, some fashioned from long-lasting oak and others carved from hard-wearing teak – all of them satin-lined and the very latest in coffin-comfort.

But it had been a very long day. As he sipped a glass of tomato juice well-doused with warming Worcester sauce, and nibbled a juicy nectarine, the Count's chin drooped onto his chest and the magazine slid slowly from his grasp.

In no time at all, Count Alucard was fast asleep. . .

"Ah-Whoo-OOO . . .!"

The howls of the wolf-pack rose on the Transylvanian crisp night air and drifted through the pine trees. The floor of the forest, as always at this time of the year, was thick with snow.

"Ah-Whooo-OOO . . .!"

The black bat's pointed ears pricked eagerly at the sound while its nostrils twitched with excitement. Still in its upside-down position, the furry-bodied creature unfurled its parchment-like wings, loosed its claw-hold on the ivied castle wall and launched itself into the darkness.

The wolves, both adults and their young, kept tight formation as they hurtled first through snow-drift then through flashing mountain stream, and seemed not to notice the black shape which had joined them and was scudding over their heads. But there could be no doubt that the bat – or Count Alucard, to give the vampire its true identity – was relishing their company.

There was absolutely nothing in the entire world, the Count told himself as he levelled out at a speed which would keep him nose-above-nose with the pack-leader wolf, quite so grand as being in the company of wolves. . .

Snug in his coffin in his bedroom at Laburnum Towers, Count Alucard snored gently and smiled as he dreamed of pleasant times in the past, spent with his friends, 'the children of the night', in the vast and snowbound Forest of Tolokovin.

"Ah-Whoo-OOO-oooooh . . .!"

6

"Miao-OOO-ooow . . .!"

"Stop it, Cazzy!" said Hilton Hargreaves, not unkindly, as the family cat, which he had just let in through the French window, rubbed its fur against his bare ankles.

It was not quite dawn. The patio and the garden beyond shone silver in the moonlight. Cazelot, the ginger cat which had been named after the young Customs man's commanding officer, had spent all night on the tiles and was hungry for an early breakfast.

"Miao-OOO-ooow . . .!"

"I said 'Stop it!' " repeated Hargreaves, glancing down past his Paisley-patterned dressing-gown towards his feet – and regretting having done so. He was wearing the panda-faced slippers that he hated and their black-dot plastic eyes were jiggling up at him tormentingly.

"Breakfast's ready!" said Thora Hargreaves, Hilton's mother, as she crossed from the kitchen stove and slipped a boiled egg off a tablespoon into the egg-cup which was waiting to collect it. "There you are," Thora continued, "now tell me *that* one's overcooked?"

"*Benissimo* this morning, Mum!" exclaimed Hilton enthusiastically, as he cracked open the egg and peered down at the golden, runny yolk. "Just right for dipping soldiers," he added, as he reached for a slice of toast from the toast-rack.

"I don't know why you had to get up *so* early," chided Mrs Hargreaves as she poured out two cups of tea. "It *is* Saturday morning. You could have had a nice long lie-in this morning."

"I told you why I wanted to get up early, Mum, before I went to bed last night. I'm catching the first bus into town this morning. I'm going to the shopping mall to buy myself a pair of slippers."

"But you've got a perfectly good pair of slippers on your feet at this moment, Hilton," his mother replied, shaking her head despairingly.

"They've got panda faces on them, Mum!"

"And for a *very* good reason, Hilton. They were bought in aid of a *very* good cause. Pandas are an endangered species. Your Aunt Edith bought those slippers in 'Adopt-A-Panda-Year'. Some of the money she spent on those slippers, Hilton, will go towards providing some poor panda with eucalyptus leaves."

The Customs man did not reply. He was not normally an uncaring person but, at that particular moment, remembering all the embarrassment the slippers had caused him the young Customs officer would not have worried if the panda his Aunt Edith had adopted did not set eyes on another eucalyptus leaf for the rest of its days.

"Besides," continued Mrs Hargreaves, "what are we to tell Aunt Edith if she should chance to call and find that you're not wearing the slippers that she bought you?" Hilton Hargreaves held his silence but his mother continued to pursue her theme. "And even if you *do* insist on buying yourself new slippers, Hilton, that's still no reason for your getting up at the crack of dawn. The shopping mall won't be opening for hours – and even when it does open, it will stay open all day long? Surely the shopping mall can wait?"

But the Customs officer, refusing to be drawn into an argument, said not one word – at least, not out loud. Perhaps the shopping mall could wait, he told himself, but *he* certainly had no intention of doing so. He would be waiting outside the shopping mall when the huge iron-gates swung open. He would be the very first customer into the shoe shop too. While other shoppers spent their time gazing into the shoe shop window, wondering which of the items on display might best suit their feet, Hilton Hargreaves already knew *exactly* what he was going to buy: a pair of size $8\frac{1}{2}$ tartan slippers with a cosy fleecy lining – the kind of slippers a chap wouldn't mind being caught wearing (should he chance to set off to work in them one morning), either on the bus or even at the airport, while doing duty in the Nothing To Declare Green Channel . . .

"MiaO-OOO-ooouw . . .!"

Lost in thought, Hilton Hargreaves barely noticed as Cazelot, the ginger tabby, again rubbed up its fur against his ankles underneath the table. Dreamily, the young Customs man dipped his toasted soldier deep into his runny egg – so deep, in fact, that the delicious golden yolk oozed up and over and down the side of the egg-shell, but Hilton did not seem to care.

While her only son day-dreamed about the new pair of slippers, Mrs Hargreaves switched on the television set in the hope of seeing a film star or a TV celebrity talking about his or her exciting glitzy show-biz lifestyle – instead of which she saw a glum-faced newscaster delivering a warning bulletin about the possibility of there being a dangerous vampire at large somewhere in the north of England. It was not at all the kind of thing that Thora Hargreaves wanted to hear about so early in the morning.

"Vampires indeed!" sniffed Mrs Hargreaves, pulling a face and turning off the telly. "Why is it always doom and gloom on the early news? Why can't they start the day by telling us about something *nice* that's happened for a change?"

"Dunno, Mum," said Hilton who had not been listening.

'CREEPY COUNT CONS CUSTOMS MEN!' it said in big black letters right across the top of the front page of that morning's newspaper and, underneath, in slightly smaller letters: 'TRANSYLVANIAN TERROR TORMENTS TERMINAL TWO!'

But Archie Oliver, the police inspector, did not give either one of these amazing headlines so much as a passing glance as he picked the newspaper off a chair and spread its separate pages across the dining-room table.

"Come on, my girl!" he said. "Come on, my little beauty!"

Upon which command, Trixiebelle the Third, the snow-white tight-curled prize-winning French poodle, leaped obediently out of her basket with a single "Woof!" and up into her proud owner's arms. Archie Oliver placed Trixiebelle gently on the outspread newspaper pages, in readiness for her final grooming before setting out for the local dog show.

"It's all right for some!" said Mrs Oliver, good-humouredly, as she glanced into the dining-room on her way out of the house. Unlike her lucky husband, who did not have to report for duty that day, Rita Oliver had to go to work. "You haven't seen this morning's newspaper by any remote chance, have you, Archie?" she said as she arranged a headscarf over her hair.

"Haven't set eyes on it," replied Police Inspector Oliver, absent-mindedly forgetting that he had spread it out across the table only a minute or so before. "Look in the kitchen."

"I haven't got the time. I'll take my library book

instead. And *do* try not to get talcum powder all over the carpet and the furniture, Archie," she added with a long-suffering sigh. "I vacuumed and polished in here only yesterday."

Mrs Oliver had spoken too late. As the front door closed behind her, her husband was hidden in a white cloud of baby powder which he had sprinkled too enthusiastically over Trixiebelle the Third. It was Archie Oliver's practice to cover the poodle in talcum powder which he then brushed off before setting out for a dog show.

The white cloud billowed up as far as the ceiling, filled the room and then settled slowly everywhere – like a snowstorm in a glass paperweight –

covering the furniture, the carpet, Trixiebelle the Third and even Archie Oliver himself in a fine film of talcum powder. The powder also settled on the newspaper which was spread out across the table, hiding the headlines about the vampire from the police inspector's sight.

Archie Oliver hummed happily to himself as he brushed energetically at the poodle's fur, for there was nothing that he enjoyed so much as a day out at a dog show. The inspector was completely unaware that the news of the vampire's arrival had hit the national headlines.

"Still, Wolf! Stand still, boy!" cried Granville Cazelot to his German Shepherd dog.

Wolf, who had won eight prizes for obedience, needed no second bidding. At his master's command, the dog stood as still and silent as a statue while Chief Customs Officer Cazelot went to work on him, in preparation for the dog show, with steel comb and stiff wire brush.

Like his good friend, Police Inspector Oliver, Granville Cazelot was also in ignorance of the nation's mounting concern regarding the monster's presence. And this despite the fact that the radio was switched on in the Cazelot bungalow while the news about the vampire was being broadcast. But Granville Cazelot was not indoors when that vital piece of information was relayed to the nation.

Clara Cazelot, his wife, was not quite as easy-going as her good friend, Rita Oliver. Mrs Cazelot was a house-proud lady and there was a strict rule in the Cazelot home, laid down by Clara, that her husband had to do all of the dog's grooming outside in the back garden. On Mrs Cazelot's behalf though, it must be stated that she did her best to warn her husband about the dangers he might have to face.

"Granville!" called Clara Cazelot sharply out of the bungalow's bedroom window. "Did you know that Dracula's turned up in England, apparently?"

"You don't say so, dear?" the Customs officer called back.

"You don't say so, dear?" were the words that Granville Cazelot always used when he wasn't paying any attention to what his wife was trying to tell him. "You don't say so, dear?" was a sure sign that the chief Customs man had not taken in one single word that Clara Cazelot had said.

"Apparently – they've just announced it on the radio. He arrived in England yesterday," continued Mrs Cazelot who, in moments of stress, either began or ended most of her sentences with the word 'apparently'. When she was feeling particularly stressed, Clara sometimes managed an 'apparently' both at the beginning and the end: "Apparently the police have lost all track of him and he could be lurking *anywhere*, up some dark alley, waiting to pounce – apparently."

"You don't say so, dear?" called back Granville Cazelot as he applied all of his concentration to his task, making broad sweeping strokes across Wolf's already gleaming flanks with the wire brush. Thoroughly enjoying the job, and relishing the day ahead, the Customs officer began to sing softly to himself as he brushed, and brushed – and brushed. . .

Monty Wilson, the obliging taxi-driver, drummed his fingers on the steering-wheel in time to the merry tune that he was whistling as he guided his cab towards the outskirts of the town and the address where his passengers were waiting to be collected.

The radio in Monty's taxi had been switched on when the news report about the vampire had been broadcast. But, like Granville Cazelot, Monty Wilson had not been paying any attention. His thoughts had strayed to more important matters.

It was Saturday morning and, after picking up and delivering his waiting passengers to their destination, it was the taxi-driver's intention to take the rest of the day off. It *was* Saturday, after all, and he had been out on the road since early morning. He would spend the rest of the morning and, hopefully, the afternoon as well, in search of antique corkscrews to add to his collection. There were several back-street junk shops that he hadn't investigated for a month or two and also a Saturday street market which had been known to come up trumps . . .

"I think it's wonderful," said Sylvia Cresswell, stepping back as far as the sofa in order to get a better view.

"It's not bad, is it, Sylvia?" said Arthur Cresswell, modestly.

Mr and Mrs Cresswell were admiring Christopher Columbus Sets Sail, the 1500 piece jigsaw puzzle which Arthur had succeeded in putting together on the dining-table while his wife had been away and soaking up the sun. Apart from the flag-ship, the Santa Maria, which had Christopher Columbus himself standing on the poop-deck, one hand on the tiller and the other shading his eyes against the sun as he gazed out towards the horizon, the jigsaw puzzle was mostly sea and sky – it must have been a very difficult puzzle to complete.

"You are a marvel, Arthur, you really are," said Sylvia Cresswell as she glanced in admiration at her husband. "I could stand here and look at it all day. It's like a work of art. It's such a pity that it's got to be taken to pieces."

"You can't make an omelette, Sylvia, without breaking eggs," observed Mr Cresswell philosophically. "If we're going to make a start on Captain Scott At The South Pole, I'm afraid that Christopher Columbus will have to go back inside his box."

"Yes, Arthur," said Sylvia Cresswell with a glum little sigh and shaking her head. "But will you be the one to make a start at taking it to pieces? I haven't got the heart."

Arthur Cresswell chuckled softly to himself as he picked the empty Christopher Columbus box off the sofa. Sylvia *was* funny, he told himself. After all the years that they had been married, after all the hundreds upon hundreds of jigsaw puzzles they had done together, Sylvia still could not bear to see a good picture puzzle being broken up. Arthur himself was just the opposite. Fitting the pieces together was the part that fascinated him – not the end result. Like any true jigsaw puzzle fanatic, as soon as one puzzle was completed, he was fretting to begin the next.

Just as Mr Cresswell had put the empty box on the table and was about to start breaking up a corner of the jigsaw puzzle, the front doorbell rang out, urgently.

"It can't be that time, surely?" gasped Sylvia.

"I'm afraid it is, Syl," said Arthur, glancing at his watch.

"But I'm still wearing my dressing-gown and jim-jams!"

"You know what they say, love," replied Arthur, nodding at the jigsaw puzzle. "Time doesn't half go fast when you're enjoying yourself. You pop upstairs and make yourself look decent – I'll answer the doorbell and tell him to hang on."

As Sylvia Cresswell hared for the stairs, her husband crossed into the hall and opened the front door.

"Good morning, sir," said Monty Wilson who was standing on the doorstep. "I believe you booked a taxi?"

Although Steven Wilkins, the Customs officer, lived by himself he was not a lonely person. Anything but. For no matter in which direction he allowed his eyes to stray in his little flat, there were goodness-only-knows how many varieties of tropical fish gazing solemnly back at Steven, unblinking, their mouths opening and shutting silently behind the glass of their illuminated homes. There were not only fish tanks in the living-room, the Customs man also kept fish both in his

85

bedroom and in the kitchen. Stevie Wilkins considered each and every single fish in his well-stocked aquarium to be his friend.

Usually, whenever he had an off-duty weekend, the Customs officer spent his Saturday in cleaning out the tanks and attending to his fishes, other needs – but on that particular Saturday morning, Stevie had another engagement to fulfill.

"Cheerio, lads—" he called out from the door of his flat, in a voice which was loud enough to carry into every fish tank, "—and lasses!" he added, in order that not a single one of the occupants of his several tanks should feel left out.

Then, carefully locking the front door of the flat behind him, Steven paused only long enough to adjust his tie and fasten the gold buttons on his smart, navy-blue blazer with its impressive Aquarium Club badge sewn onto the breast pocket, before setting out in some haste.

As usual, the lift was out of order and Stevie's echoing footsteps clattered up the stairwell as he raced down towards the entrance hall, taking two stairs at a time . . .

"Are you *quite* sure that you wouldn't like a cup of coffee and a ginger biccie, Ronnie?" asked Julia Fairhurst.

"No, ta," replied her husband. "I'd rather make a start and get it finished."

"I can't wait to see it when it's up," said Julia with a happy smile as she picked up the cup of coffee she had made for herself and went out into the sitting-room, the packet of ginger biscuits in her other hand.

Alone in the kitchen, Ronnie Fairhurst pulled a face and his eyes blinked several times behind his glasses as he contemplated the difficult task his wife had set him.

There had been something exciting and important that the Customs officer had set his heart on doing – but Julia had come up with her own idea as to how he should spend his leisure hours that Saturday morning. Which was why Ronnie Fairhurst found himself in a pair of overalls and with a box of tools, about to practise his DIY skills at assembling and putting up a spice-rack on the kitchen wall. Taking the sheet of paper out of its plastic wrapper, Ronnie unfolded the complicated instructions and squinted at them through his glasses.

Julia Fairhurst, in the living-room, snuggled down in the comfiest chair. There were domestic chores that she too had to perform that morning – a huge pile of ironing in the basket in the utility room and she hadn't the faintest idea yet about what to cook for lunch – but Mrs Fairhurst wasn't in a hurry. First of all, she had promised herself, she was going to enjoy the luxury of the cup of coffee, two ginger biscuits and another chapter of the detective novel she was currently reading. Julia was an avid fan of all mystery stories but particularly those which concerned the adventures of the ace private eye, Sefton Marchbanks.

Dipping a ginger biscuit into her coffee, Julia turned to the page where she had placed the bookmark before switching off the bedside light the night before, and began to read:

Marchbanks' brow was furrowed as he glanced around the croquet lawn at Radleigh Manor. His keen sixth sense told him that everything was not quite as it should be. And then his frown dissolved into a smile as his detective's eagle eyes fixed on the discarded match-book cover which seemed entirely out of place on the neatly trimmed and usually litter-free croquet lawn. The famous detective strode across, stooped, and picked up the empty book of matches. Across its front cover were printed the words: 'The Flamingo Night Club'.

"What a stroke of luck!" Sefton Marchbanks murmured to himself as he slipped the match-book cover into his pocket for safekeeping. "This could be the very clue that may help me solve the mystery of Lord Symington's disappearance. . ."

Julia Fairhurst glanced up from *The Murders On The Croquet Lawn* and cocked her head on one side as she listened carefully – and heard not so much as a sound. But it had been that very same silence that had disturbed her concentration. Why was there no noise coming from her husband as he struggled at putting the new spice-rack together?

Slipping the bookmark back inside the pages, Julia put down her book, rose from her chair and tiptoed quietly into the kitchen. The room was empty. The spice-rack, still unassembled, and the box of tools were on the kitchen floor, together with a pair of discarded overalls – but Ronnie Fairhurst, who had been wearing the overalls, was no longer there.

"Ronnie?" Julia called out loudly, in case her

husband might have gone upstairs to 'spend a penny'. "*Ron*! Are you in the lavvy?"

But there was no reply and the Fairhurst house was ominously still and silent. Julia gave a little gasp and shuddered slightly. It was as if her husband had been spirited off or else had vanished into thin air.

It was just the kind of mystery that Sefton Marchbanks would have liked to have got his teeth into, thought Julia. She tried to imagine herself inside the famous detective's shoes. What would *he* have done in such a situation? Of course! He would have looked for clues. Julia allowed her eyes to stray slowly over the kitchen floor and, sure enough, she spotted a small object she had not previously noticed. Striding across, she stooped and picked up the item that had caught her eye and which, on closer examination, turned out to be a corner piece of a jigsaw puzzle. Examining it more closely still, Julia decided that the bit of jigsaw had come from a puzzle which depicted some sort of castle wall.

"What a stroke of luck!" she murmured, unintentionally echoing her fictional hero's words. "This could be the clue that helps me solve the mystery of Ronnie's disappearance."

Slipping the jigsaw puzzle piece inside her purse for safekeeping, Julia Fairhurst next sought out that morning's newspaper. A cold shiver ran up her back as she took in the front page headlines about the vampire. But quickly dismissing the thought that Count Dracula might have had a hand in her husband's disappearance, Julia turned to the inside

89

pages and the 'Weekend Events' column.

Her forefinger shook with excitement as it ran down the list of local happenings – for an inner sixth sense told her that the column might provide her with another step forward in her search for her missing husband.

"Where *are* we going, Dad?" asked Henry Hollins.

"Ah-hah!" said Albert Hollins mysteriously, as he steered the family car along a country road towards the destination he was yet to reveal. "That would be telling, Henry."

"Do *you* know where we're going, Mum?"

"It's no good asking me, Henry," replied Emily with a small shrug of her shoulders and a little sigh. "I know no more than you do. You know what your dad's like when he's got something he wants to keep to himself – wild horses couldn't drag it out of him."

"I do know how to keep a secret," said Albert Hollins proudly. "It's one of the first things that you have to promise to do when you're a member of Staplewood Magic Club – not to reveal the tricks of the magic trade to anyone."

"But you're *not* a member of the Staplewood Magic Club, Albert," said Mrs Hollins. "They wouldn't let you join – you didn't pass your audition."

"Not on that first occasion, no," said Mr Hollins rather crossly. "But what you don't seem to appreciate, Emily, is that joining the Magic Club is like learning how to drive a car – hardly anyone

90

passes their driving test at the first time of asking, do they?"

"I did," said Emily proudly.

"That's not the point," snapped Albert. "The thing is that I'll have to do another audition – but for the time being, they've made me a probationary member."

"Is that like having an L plate, Dad?" asked Henry.

"Sort of – and I'll pass the audition at next month's meeting – just you wait and see."

Mr Hollins lapsed into silence and concentrated on the road ahead. Wisely, both Emily and Henry did not pursue the subject of the Staplewood Magic Club either. The club met on the first Wednesday of every month in the Community Centre. Anyone wishing to join the club had to perform a five minute magic act on the Community Centre stage, in front of the entire membership. It was a daunting prospect and that first audition was something of a sore point still with Albert Hollins. It was not something that he cared to discuss – or even liked to think about. Unfortunately though, it was something he found difficult to forget. . .

To this day, as he tried to concentrate his thoughts on driving the car, Albert Hollins could hear the sniggers of the badly-behaved members of the Staplewood Magic Club ringing in his head. . .

While Albert Hollins attempted to dispel the memory of that awful audition, Emily was also lost in reverie. But unlike her husband, Emily's thoughts were entirely pleasant ones. She was recalling the wonderful moment when she had raced along the garden path and then burst into the house, waving the precious slip of paper above her head and calling out those wonderful words: "I've passed! I've passed!" Mr Hollins, who had needed three attempts before passing *his* driving test, had glanced up over the top of his newspaper, cleared his throat and managed a "Well done, Emily" and muttered something to himself about "driving tests being easier these days". Henry had clapped his hands with glee and cried: "Ace, Mum! Terrific!"

Henry, sitting in the back of the car, was also deep in thought. But his concerns were not for himself – not for the first time over the last couple of days, he was worried about the welfare and the whereabouts of his best friend, Count Alucard, the Transylvanian vegetarian vampire. . .

"Ah-Whooo-OOO . . .!"

The wolves, howling in unison and without pause, stretched their legs and increased pace as they raced onwards through the untrodden snow, deeper and deeper towards the heart of the Tolokovin Forest. Charging through drifts and gullies, sometimes skidding over ice-bound streams, under the moon's pale light they revelled in the sheer delight of being alive. While all the time, in the network of pine branches overhead, Count Alucard, the vegetarian vampire bat, was constant companion to the wolf-pack as he flitted and fluttered on dark parchment-like wings – sometimes skimming down so close that he almost touched the greying fur on the grizzled pack-leader's head.

"Ah-whooo-OOO . . .!"

Although the morning was well-advanced, the sun high up in the sky and the rest of the hotel out of bed and about its business, Count Alucard lay fast asleep, snug in the peaceful warmth of his satin-lined coffin.

The bedroom curtains were shut tight, blocking out the daylight, and the Count was unaware that he had drastically overslept as he dreamed fond dreams about past nights spent in his homeland.

7

Although Rita Oliver often led her police inspector husband to believe the absolute opposite, the truth of the matter was that she *really* enjoyed her Saturday job.

For one thing, and thank goodness, it got her out of the house sufficiently early in the morning to avoid having to swallow the clouds of talcum powder that Archie was constantly launching over Trixiebelle the Third. Mrs Oliver was a martyr to hay fever and swallowing talcum powder always aggravated the complaint. Best of all though, Rita Oliver relished her post as a Saturday shop-assistant because it brought her into contact with the general public. Rita's hobby, as she once informed the entire population of the United Kingdom, was 'meeting people'.

It should be explained, perhaps, that Rita Oliver was almost famous. She had once been on a TV game show called *Fancy That!* During the programme, Benny Benson, the show's presenter, had asked Rita if she had any hobbies? "Meeting people," Mrs Oliver had instantly replied. Although she had only appeared on the programme once, had not won a major prize nor heard those exciting words "Can you come back next week?" – she still enjoyed the occasional person coming into the shop and almost recognising her. "Haven't I seen you somewhere before?" the customer would ask. "You might have seen me on the telly – I was on *Fancy That!*" was always Rita's proud reply.

Rita enjoyed being almost famous. It was also true that she liked meeting people. And there was no better way of meeting people than having a Saturday job as a shop-assistant. Of course, she did have to put up with the occasional nasty customer for whom there was no pleasing but, for the most part, the people that came into the En-Vee Shoe Shop were pleasant folk who knew exactly what they wanted – and were appreciative when Rita was able to help.

Like, for instance, the shy young man who had spent a quarter of an hour that very morning, peering into the shop window before daring to venture through the door.

"Yes, sir," said Rita, crossing with a smile towards this latest customer. "Can I be of any assistance?"

"I shouldn't think so," replied Hilton Hargreaves with a doleful sigh. "I'm looking for a pair of size $8\frac{1}{2}$ tartan slippers with a fleecy lining – I've already been to that big store in the shopping mall – and to Fearing's Footwear Specialists in the High Street – but neither of them had anything in stock in my size—" At which point, the Customs officer broke off to peer at the shop-assistant closely, before adding: "Excuse me asking, but don't I know you from somewhere?"

"You don't know me personally," replied Rita with a shake of her head. "But you might have seen me on the telly – I was on *Fancy That!*"

"Wow!" went Hilton Hargreaves suitably impressed. "Were you really? What's he like, Benny Benson, when you meet him in real life?"

"He's very nice," said Rita Oliver, happy to reveal the inner secrets of her brush with show business. "We had a drink with him afterwards in the studio canteen – me and the other two contestants. They gave us a glass of medium-dry white wine, some bite-size dinky pizzas and there were sausages-on-sticks as well."

"Wow-eeEE!" He was even more impressed. He paused before venturing his next rather delicate question: "Can I ask you something – is it his real hair or does he wear a wig?"

"I don't know," replied Rita Oliver thoughtfully. "But you're not the first person to ask." Then, deciding that she had revealed more than enough about the private life of the famous TV celebrity, Rita Oliver changed the subject. "About your tartan slippers . . ."

"Don't tell me," said Hilton Hargreaves, glumly. "You're going to say that you haven't got any in my size either, aren't you?"

"I'm afraid not," said Rita Oliver then, broadening her smile she added: "But I think I know where you might just be lucky . . ."

"Ah-Whooo-OOO . . ."
Man and boy, Count Alucard had grown up with

96

the wolf-pack which hunted in the Tolokovin Forest surrounding Alucard Castle. In his childhood, in the best of summers, he had frolicked with the wolf cubs in the shade of the castle's ivied walls. In the worst of winters, he had seen to it that the wolves never went hungry – filching food from under the cooks' noses to meet the wolf-pack's needs. Once, when he was very young and had foolishly strayed from a forest track, it had been the wolf-pack leader that had guided him safely back to the castle gate. The wolves were his friends, each and every one of them.

And why not? He and the wolves had much in common. They were both misunderstood and feared by the human race. Wolves had never been known to attack human beings – unless the human beings had startled or attacked them first. And, of a certainty, Count Alucard had never knowingly harmed any one of God's creatures. And yet the human race had decided, in its ignorance, that both the wolves and he himself were its natural enemies. Count Alucard often wondered why . . .?

But at magical times such as these, in the dark of the star-studded night, in the heart of the snow-covered Transylvanian pine forest, skimming along in company with his fleet-footed friends, such matters as the perversity of humankind seemed totally unimportant . . .

"Ah-WhoooOOO . . .!"

And this time the howling penetrated Count Alucard's mind and he sat up so suddenly that he almost banged his head on the top edge of his coffin. Realising where he was, the Count allowed himself a slow, sad smile. He had been dreaming

97

once again about the old days and the delightful Transylvanian winter nights. Blinking into wakefulness, he glanced around at his Laburnum Towers bedroom.

Although the curtains were tightly drawn, there was a chink of sunlight creeping in and Count Alucard suspected that he must have overslept. Small wonder though, he told himself, considering his previous hectic day. Reaching across to the bedside table, he picked up the exquisite filigree gold watch which had belonged to his father, and to his father's father before him and which he had set down, carefully, the night before.

"Mercy me!" murmured the Count as he glanced at the watch-face. It was so long past breakfast that it was almost time for lunch.

"Ah-Whooo-OOO . . .!"

"Just wait one tiny moment," Count Alucard puzzled to himself. If the wolves had been a part of his dream, why were they howling still in his waking life?

"Ah-Whooo-OOO . . .!"

There it was again! And this time, of a certainty, the Count told himself, it was certainly no dream. Slipping his pale, slim feet over the rim of the coffin, he lowered them to the carpet. Then, levering himself upright, he tiptoed across and tugged at the cord which drew back the curtains. The sunlight flooded in so suddenly that the Count stood dazzled for several seconds. Then, after lifting the catch and opening the window, he poked out his head and peered down into the hotel's grounds.

"Ah-Whooo-OOO . . .!"

Count Alucard gasped and blinked in wonder at the sight that met his eyes, and then blinked a second time.

"Ah-Whooo-OOO . . .!"

When he had retired into his coffin the night before, his bedroom, situated on the top floor and at the back of the hotel, had overlooked a vast expanse of well-trimmed lawn. Now, in the morning sunlight, the entire area was a mass of bunting-bedecked marquees, tents, awnings, caravans and partitioned canvas alleyways – but most of all, it seemed to be alive with dogs.

There were dogs of all shapes and sizes. Big dogs, medium-sized dogs, short elongated dogs whose stomachs brushed the ground. There were long-haired dogs; there were short-haired dogs; there were dogs with coats so smooth and shiny that it seemed as if they had no fur at all. There were rough-haired dogs; there were tousled dogs; there were dogs so small and dainty that they would have fitted comfortably into the palm of a hand. There were dogs with elegant tails that touched the ground and dogs with stumpy tails that wagged enthusiastically and never seemed to stop.

Count Alucard had never seen so many different kinds of dogs at one and the same time before. They were, for the most part, well-behaved dogs that patiently ignored each other's presence – as if they had sat in close proximity to each other a hundred times before.

"Ah-Whoo-OOOOOOO . . .!"

The Count realised, to his surprise, that it was just one dog that was responsible for all the racket. While all the others sat incredibly still as they waited for their owners to groom them, a large German Shepherd dog was standing on all fours, its head thrown back, its jaws wide open, fangs bared, as it howled – and howled – and howled again. . . .

"Ah-Whooo-OOOOOOooooooh . . .!"

"I wonder," mused the Count to himself, "whether it might be my presence in the hotel that is causing that poor creature's distress?"

Back in his native Transylvania, the wolves that roamed the Forest of Tolokovin were similarly nervous whenever they sensed that the Count was indoors in his family home. All day long, the pack would howl and prowl outside the castle's ivied walls – satisfied only when evening drifted into night and Count Alucard was then able to assume his bat-form and swoop down from out of his bedroom window to join his four-legged friends below.

It was possible, the Count told himself, that the German Shepherd dog on the lawn beneath his hotel window – a near-relative, surely, of the wolf – could also sense a vampire's presence and that he himself was responsible for the animal's howls?

"Ah-Whooo-OOOOOOooooooh . . .!"

Count Alucard hastily drew his head back inside the bedroom and closed the window tight. But the damage had been done, it seemed, and the howling continued.

"Ah-Whooo-OOOOOOooooooh . . .!"

"Belt up, Wolf!" snapped Granville Cazelot at his German Shepherd dog. It was quite unlike the dog to misbehave and the off-duty Customs chief glanced round in some embarrassment at the nearby fellow dog-owners who were beginning to give him and his pet some curious glances.

"Having problems with your Alsatian, Granville?" asked Archie Oliver, trying hard not to grin at his chum's discomfiture. The off-duty police inspector was standing close at hand and fastening a red ribbon bow between the pricked ears of Trixiebelle the Third.

"Ah-Whooo-oooOOOH . . .!"

"I said 'Belt up!' " snarled the Customs chief and then, turning to the police inspector, he continued: "He's not an Alsatian, Archie, as well you know – he's a pedigree German Shepherd, and I'll thank you to give him his proper title. And, yes, I am

101

having problems. I can't think what's got into him. He's never behaved like this before."

"Ah-Whooo-OOO-ooooOOOOH . . .!"

It was bound to happen, of course. Wolf's agitation was, at last, beginning to affect several of the dog show's entrants, some of whom were sniffing anxiously at the air while others scraped their hind-quarters on the floor of their canvas stalls. But it was Police Inspector Oliver's Trixiebelle the Third that was the first dog to imitate the German Shepherd dog and give noisy vent to her feelings:

"Yelp! Yelp! Yelp . . .!" went the French poodle, lifting her beribboned curly head, opening her jaws and snappishly yelping at the top of her bark.

"Having problems with your poodle, Archie?" asked Granville Cazelot with a smirk.

"Hush up, Trixie, there's a good girl," said Oliver then, turning to the Customs chief, he continued: "If I am, Granville, it's only because your badly behaved Alsatian has set her off!"

"How many times must I tell you, Archie, that he's a German Shepherd dog, *not* an Alsatian!"

But before the argument could develop, more dogs began to join in with the chorus, one by one, each of them letting out a sound to match its size and temperament.

"Grrrr! Grrrrrr . . .!" growled a British bulldog.

"Give over, Winston!" growled its owner, a short, stocky, red-faced man in a check-suit.

"Yap! Yap! Yap . . .!" snapped a pair of Pekingese.

"Ching-Ching! Wan-Toon! Stop that this

102

instant!" snapped a fussy, pinch-faced lady.

"Woof-woof! Woof-woof...!" went a wire-haired Yorkshire terrier.

"Hey up, Trueman! We'll have less o' that, lad!" went its owner, a small skinny man with a straggling moustache.

"Ah-ruff! Ah-ruff...!" barked an Irish wolfhound.

"If yez don't pack that blather in, O'Flaherty, yez'll be in more trouble than yez bargained for!" barked its owner, a tall, green-eyed, no-nonsense lady.

But the dogs paid not the slightest attention to any of this and, in seconds, more entrants in the show had joined in the chorus, all of them barking at once and with their owners unable to get a word in edgewise.

"Ah-Whooo-OOO-oooOOOH! Grrrr! Grrrrrr! Yelp! Yelp! Yelp! Woof-Woof! Woof-Woof! Yap! Yap! Yap! Ah-ruff! Ah-ruff! Ah-Whooo-OOO-oooOOOH...!"

Bedlam reigned supreme.

Dressed in his monogrammed silk pyjamas, Count Alucard sat miserably on the edge of the bed, his head held in his hands and gloomily curling his toes. There was no doubt in the Transylvanian nobleman's mind that he himself was the reason for the kerfuffle outside in the hotel gardens.

Although the Count was proud of his family name, there *were* times when he regretted being a vampire. This was one of them. It seemed that he could not go anywhere without being the cause of some upset. Usually, his presence sparked off fear and loathing in the human race – but here he had managed to disrupt a harmless gathering of four-footed animals!

As the howls increased outside, in volume and in number, the Count decided that it might be best for all – himself included – if he were to take his leave of Laburnum Towers and as soon as possible. But where could he go, he asked himself? Well, there was one person in the world, at least, who was always pleased to see him. . . .

Opening the wardrobe, the Count felt in the inside pocket of his jacket and took out his Vampire's Diary. He flicked through the several pages of Useful Information at the front – past the one which contained the dates of that year's Transylvanian full moons and the addresses of emergency blood banks around the world – and

stopped at the next page where he had written down his most important telephone numbers. Running a forefinger hastily down the list, he slowed when he came to *Hoffmeister & Sons, Coffin Manufacturers to the European Nobility*, and then stopped at the next name he came to.

"Brrrr-brrrr! Brrrr-brrrr. . . ." The telephone on the hall table at No. 42 Nicholas Nickleby Close, Stapleford, rang out underneath the brightly coloured telephone-cover which Emily Hollins had knitted for the instrument. But as there was not one member of the Hollins family at home to answer it, the telephone went on ringing. ". . . .Brrrr-brrrr! Brrr-brrrr. . . ."

Receiving no answer, Count Alucard let out a small sigh of desperation as he replaced the bedside telephone. Henry Hollins, his one true friend, was not at home and he had no idea who he could turn to next. Meanwhile, the howling of the dogs outside was growing ever louder. There was no time to be lost. He would just have to pack his coffin as quickly as he could and take himself off again into the unkind, unfriendly world outside.

Carefully folding his pyjama jacket, the Count laid it neatly inside his coffin before taking a clean, starched, frilly-fronted, white silk dress-shirt from out of a drawer and unfastening the buttons ready for it to be put on.

One thing that no man could deny was the fact

that no matter how much trouble the Count was in, or no matter how much anguish he was forced to suffer, he was never less than impeccably dressed from head to toe. His white bow tie was always neatly tied, there was never less than a knife-edge crease in his smart black trousers, and his shoes were always so highly polished that he could see his face reflected in them – that is to say, of course, that he *would* have been able to observe his face had he been so fortunate as to possess a reflection.

Crossing into the bathroom, the Count stepped out of his pyjama trousers and into the shower cubicle, closing the door behind him. Moments later, as he soaped himself under the jet of hot water, he bolstered his spirits by raising his voice and singing a folk song which his father had taught him as a child. It was a song about a little Transylvanian boy and his friendship with a pack of wolves and, whenever the Count heard it sung, tears came into his eyes – but they were tears not of sadness but of joy.

> "*Sovra zora,*
> *Sovoba dovra-dovrey,*
> *Sovra zokra,*
> *Sovela zokrato. . . .*"

Although he had not the faintest idea where he could go once he had checked out of the hotel – or who, if anyone, he could turn to for assistance – Count Alucard did not intend to allow the bleakness of his situation to defeat him. For though he was given to suffering despairing clouds of gloom when things weren't going well, he did not allow such moments to get the better of him for very long.

Besides, so long as he was singing at the top of his voice, and so long as he kept the shower turned full on, the sound of the dogs barking on the lawn below his window was completely drowned out.

> '*Sovra hobra,*
> *Sovora dovra-dushka,*
> *Sovra zokra,*
> *Sovora dushka-HOY . . .!*"

Count Alucard's cheeks were wet with tears which mingled with the droplets of water caused by the shower's spray and were quickly washed away.

"Here we are then, folks – at long last," said Monty Wilson as the taxi came to a standstill. Monty turned and winked at Sylvia and Arthur Cresswell who were sitting in the back, and added: "Apologies for the small diversion I had to make."

Instead of driving straight to the address which the Cresswells had requested, Monty had gone a long way round, calling first at a DIY store where he had bought two tins of glossy duck-egg blue paint which he had then delivered to his own home. As Monty had explained to the Cresswells en route, his wife, Freda, had got it into her head to paint the bathroom that Saturday morning. The Cresswells, it seemed, had no particular objection to taking this circuitous route.

"That's all right," said Sylvia. "At least you've got us here safe and sound."

"And in one piece," said Arthur Cresswell adding, good-humouredly: "Just so long as you don't charge us for the extra miles!"

"As if I would," chuckled Monty Wilson. It was not his usual practice to run his personal errands while he was on hire but it was Saturday and he wouldn't normally have been working. "I'll tell you what I'll do," he continued to his passengers. "We've clocked up twelve pounds fifty on the meter – what say we call it six pounds seventy-five?"

"That sounds to me like a very reasonable offer," said Arthur Cresswell as he opened the door on his side of the taxi. "Will you give the gentleman what we owe him, Sylvia, and I'll have the treasurer reimburse you later."

With his long, shabby overcoat flapping round his ankles, Arthur Cresswell got out of the taxi. Sylvia Cresswell moved to follow her husband as she fished for her purse inside her handbag. With Monty Wilson's help, Arthur Cresswell manhandled a bulky cardboard packing-case out of the taxi's boot and onto the ground.

"Whew!" gasped the cabdriver. "That weighs a ton-and-a-half! What have you got inside? Somebody's dead body?"

Arthur Cresswell gave the cabbie a mysterious smile but said nothing.

"Keep the change," said Sylvia Cresswell, handing Monty Wilson a five pound note and two one pound coins.

"Cheers – very much appreciated," said Mr

Wilson, slipping the money into a trouser-pocket and then moving back towards his driving-seat.

Sylvia crossed to stand beside her husband. Together, they stood in silence for several moments, gazing solemnly at the building that rose up before them.

"Isn't it *huge*, Arthur!" said Sylvia at last. "It's the first time I've ever been here."

"Me too."

"I've seen pictures of it in the local paper," said Sylvia. "But this is the first time I've seen it in real life."

"Photographs don't do it justice," observed Arthur Cresswell, running a hand through his spiky hair. "It's certainly a vast improvement on that dilapidated boy-scout hut we've been forced to use for our previous meetings."

"I'll bid you both a civil good-day then!" called out Monty Wilson as he started up the taxi's engine.

"Bye-bye!" replied Arthur Cresswell.

"Have a nice day yourself!" shouted Sylvia and, as the taxi moved away, she called out after it: "Drive carefully . . .!"

"Good morrow, sir! Good morrow, madam!" broke in the voice of the uniformed commissionaire who had come out to greet the Cresswells unnoticed. Stanley Groves touched his shiny peaked cap with a white-gloved hand while he held open the large glass door with the other. "I'll get one of our porters to attend to that, sir," he added, as Arthur attempted to pick up the packing-case.

Sylvia Cresswell, overawed both by the amount

of gold braid on the commissionaire's uniform and also by the hotel's gleaming magnificence, slipped a hand through her husband's arm for reassurance. Husband and wife, they moved forward nervously into the foyer of Laburnum Towers.

Monty Wilson whistled a merry tune as he strode out along the gravelled path which led towards the entrance to Laburnum Towers.

Sylvia Cresswell's parting words advising the cabbie to 'drive carefully' had not been necessary. In fact, after dropping off the Cresswells, Monty had driven his taxi no more than fifty metres or so before pulling up on the first empty space in the hotel's car-park.

"Hello again, Monty, my old pal!" called Stanley Groves as the cab-driver approached him. "I had a feeling in my bones that you'd be putting in another appearance."

"Good morning, Stan!" said Monty Wilson, giving him a friendly grin as he strolled through the door which the commissionaire was holding open.

The taxi-driver's spirits rose even higher as his eyes wandered around the bustling reception area. He felt a familiar tingle of excitement around the back of his neck inside his shirt-collar.

Things were certainly buzzing on that Saturday morning at Laburnum Towers and Monty Wilson's sixth sense told him that an exciting day lay ahead. Monty Wilson's sixth sense was seldom wrong.

8

"I do hope that the lady in that shoe shop has got her facts straight," murmured Hilton Hargreaves to himself as, in his anxiety and without being aware of what he was doing, he rolled his bus ticket into a tiny tube between his fingers and then unrolled it flat again. It would be awful, he told himself, if he had come all this way on a wild-goose chase.

The Customs officer was perched on the front seat on the top of a double-decker bus which was travelling along the city's outer ring road. But Hargreaves paid scant attention – if any at all – to his panoramic view of leafy lanes and grand houses. He was pondering the suggestion which the assistant in the En-Vee Shoe Shop had put to him.

"Laburnum Towers!"

The bus driver's cry was loud enough to carry to all parts of the vehicle and Hilton Hargreaves rose to his feet and moved unsteadily along the aisle as the bus slowed down with several jerks as it approached his destination.

"She *seemed* like a kindly and agreeable lady," Hargreaves puzzled to himself as he started down the steps which led to the platform. "Why would

111

she want to send someone that she'd never seen before on a wild-goose chase? But on the other hand, what would a posh hotel like Laburnum Towers want with—?"

The young Customs officer's ruminations came to an abrupt stop halfway down the flight of stairs as, to his surprise and consternation, he caught sight of a familiar figure standing on the platform.

"What's *he* doing on this bus? And, what's more important, why is he getting off at Laburnum Towers?" Hilton Hargreaves asked himself both of these questions as he gazed glumly at the back of Steven Wilkins' head. Wilkins, who must have been sitting downstairs, was waiting for the bus doors to open.

Luckily for Hargreaves, Steven Wilkins had his back to the stairs. Hilton Hargreaves let out a small sigh of relief at this small stroke of good fortune. If Wilkins had caught sight of him, he would have been sure to have asked him why *he* was going to Laburnum Towers. And if Hargreaves had then been forced to admit – for he was nothing if not an honest person – that he was going in search of a pair of size $8\frac{1}{2}$ fleecy-lined tartan slippers, then Wilkins would not have easily allowed him to forget it. Hilton Hargreaves had suffered more than his fair share of teasing from his fellow officers because of the unfortunate business of the panda slippers. If Stevie Wilkins were to reveal to the rest of the lads that he had discovered Hargreaves in pursuit of yet another pair of slippers and in the posh hotel, Laburnum Towers, then life would not be worth living. . . .

112

"I'll wait until he is on his way before I get off," murmured Hilton Hargreaves softly to himself as he retreated two steps backwards, out of sight, towards the upper deck.

In fact, Hargreaves need not have concerned himself at all about Wilkins' presence. Steven Wilkins' mind was too full with matters close to his own heart to have bothered himself with Hilton Hargreaves's problems. Indeed, he was so wrapped up in his personal thoughts that he did not even notice the pretty, red-haired, green-eyed, freckle-faced young woman who had come out of the lower deck, at the very last moment, and was standing close beside him.

Policewoman Sandra Simmons had also got that Saturday free from duty. She had discarded her uniform in favour of a red sweatshirt, a matching miniskirt, green stockings and a pair of sneakers. Sandra had business of her own to attend to at Laburnum Towers.

"There you go then!" called the bus driver as he pressed the button and opened the doors once the double-decker had stopped.

Steven Wilkins was first away, jumping down onto the pavement and then starting out through the two stone pillars and then along the driveway which meandered up to the front of the hotel. Some way behind the Customs officer came Sandra Simmons, striding out in pace with Wilkins, her sneakers crunching on the gravel drive. Hilton Hargreaves brought up the rear, falling further behind as he took a zigzag course, nipping through the bushes on one side of the drive and taking

113

shelter behind each tree trunk in order that Wilkins would not spot him should he chance to take a backward glance.

None of the three gave any attention to the motorcycle, its rider bent low over the handlebars, as the machine zapped past them kicking up gravel in its wake, heading towards the car park. Snug inside her tight-fitting leathers, her head encased inside her helmet, her face hidden behind her goggles, the motorcyclist did not so much as glance at either of the figures striding out along the driveway – nor did she even notice the third one taking its curious zigzag path between the trees.

Julia Fairhurst, still imagining herself in the role of Sefton Marchbanks, her favourite fictional detective, eased off the throttle on her motorcycle as she skidded into the hotel's car park. She was hot on the trail of her missing husband.

"There is *one* good thing to be said for it," Count Alucard assured himself as he knotted his white tie into a perfect bow without the aid of a mirror but with a dexterity born of long practice. "At least there is no-one in this hotel who knows me. I shall be able to walk out through the front doors without anyone giving me a second glance."

The Count was feeling much more relaxed after having had his hot shower and putting on clean underwear and a crisply ironed shirt. It also comforted him to note that the howls and barks and yaps had died down on the lawn below his window. The dogs' owners, it would seem to

114

appear, had finally succeeded in getting their pets under some sort of control.

Even so, the Count's mind was still made up. It would not be wise to dally here any longer. He would check out of the hotel and move on somewhere else. Laburnum Towers had served its purpose. But he had been wrong in thinking, the day before, that what he needed was a large hotel. Quite the opposite, in fact. No, what would suit his needs best would be somewhere *much* smaller – a boarding-house, perhaps, with himself the only guest – or he might seek out a a cosy bed-sitter. Somewhere where he could really be *alone*. Laburnum Towers was *much* too big. And *much* too busy. Why, his presence here might be discovered by any nosey-parker at any minute. . .

"Rat-a-tat-TAT!"

Count Alucard jumped with both fear and surprise at the sudden unexpected sound of knocking on his bedroom door.

"Who . . .who calls?" he enquired, tremulously.

"It's me, sir! You rang down to reception and asked them to send a porter up," said a voice outside.

Of course he had! And how foolish of him to forget. The Count paused for a second or two until his heart had stopped fluttering in his chest, then crossed and opened the door to find the friendly figure of Kevin Protheroe standing outside with his porter's trolley.

"How kind of you," began the Count, beckoning the porter inside the room and pointing to the sleek black polished coffin which was standing upright near the door. "I'm all packed and ready to move on," he said.

A minute or so later, they were in the lift at the end of the corridor and Kevin Protheroe had pressed the button which would take them down to the hotel lobby. The lift door closed silently and they were on their way. Count Alucard crossed his fingers behind his back and wished that they might reach the ground floor without taking any inquisitive passengers on board. No such luck. The lift stopped at the floor below and the door slid open to reveal three rather portly, red-cheeked, bald-headed jolly-looking gentlemen.

"Have you got room inside for three little ones?" asked the chubbiest of the trio with a friendly grin then, without waiting for an answer, he stepped into the lift, followed closely by his two companions.

It was a tight fit.

"All breathe in!" chuckled the second portly gentleman as all three just managed to squeeze themselves alongside the Count, the porter and the upright coffin.

"Who'd be a sardine?" said the third portly gentleman with a giggle and a wink.

"I say! My word! That's a beauty!" said the first man, nodding enthusiastically at the coffin which was tight up against his nose but which, curiously, did not seem to cause him any qualms whatsoever. "What does it do?" he added as the lift door closed and the descent began again.

"Not a great deal, I'm afraid," murmured Count Alucard with an apologetic shrug of his slim

116

shoulders. He did not understand the question. After all, what did any coffin 'do' apart from providing comfortable sleeping accommodation for its owner and serving as a suitcase when one travelled abroad?

Another odd fact was puzzling the Count. Why, he wondered, were the three portly gentlemen all dressed in similar fashion to himself? Each one of the trio wore a black tail coat, matching trousers, a frilly-fronted white starched shirt and a neatly knotted bow tie. One of them even had a gold medallion hanging round his neck, just like the Count, and suspended from a blue velvet ribbon. The Transylvanian vampire squinted as he peered over the second gentleman's shoulder and tried to read the medallion's inscription – but the lettering was much too small for him to decipher across the lift.

There was no way of telling who or what the trio were – one thing was certain though, the Count assured himself, they were not vampires. They were far too portly and had much too much colour in their rosy cheeks to be considered members of the Dracula clan.

"All change!" the second one called out cheerily as the lift stopped again, this time at the third floor.

The lift door slid open softly. A tall, grave, mysterious-looking Chinese gentleman was standing in the corridor. His hands were folded across his stomach and were tucked away inside the flowing sleeves of his colourful brocaded mandarin's costume. A long black pigtail hung down his back.

Count Alucard gulped and a shiver of excitement ran up his spine. He guessed that he was looking at the owner of the sinister Chinese cabinet he had heard mention of. Laburnum Towers was becoming more puzzling by the minute. First the trio of gentlemen dressed in vampire costume – and now this strange Chinese mandarin was wanting to get into the lift.

There wasn't room for him.

"You've got no chance, Ashley!" said the third portly gentleman, chuckling as he gave the mandarin a thumbs-down sign. "We're seriously overloaded as it is."

"Ashley?" the Count puzzled to himself. "*Ashley*!" What sort of a name was 'Ashley' for a mandarin?

"Would you believe it!" exclaimed the Chinese gentleman, good-humouredly, and with an accent

118

that suggested that his home town might be Birmingham rather than Beijing. "I've been stood here in this corridor, like Patience on a monument, for a good ten minutes – and when the flipping lift *does* decide to turn up, it's loaded to the gills!"

"Never mind, Ashley," said the second portly gentleman, giving Count Alucard a secretive wink. "There'll be an empty one along in no time."

"Stand well clear of the doors, please!" cried the first portly gentleman, doing his imitation of a railway guard as he pressed the 'Down' button.

Before the door slid shut, Ashley, the Chinese mandarin, put both of his hands up to his nose and wiggled his fingers at the occupants of the lift. The three portly gentlemen hooted with laughter as the lift again began its descent.

"He's a proper card, is Ashley," the third portly gentleman confided to the Count, as if they were old friends.

"He's a riot!" said the second portly gentleman.

"Did you see him last year, at Eastbourne?" asked the first portly gentleman. "When he put those handcuffs on the hotel manager – and then discovered that he hadn't brought the key with him?"

"Er – n-n-n-no . . ." stammered the Transylvanian vampire.

"How about the year before, at Harrogate?" asked the third. "When his Chinese lanterns went skewwhiff and he very nearly set the hotel on fire?"

"I'm afraid not," murmured the Count, his red-rimmed vampire's eyes bulging at what sounded to him like talk of arson.

The three portly gentlemen threw back their heads and hooted with laughter for a second time.

But the Count did not join them in their merriment. What *was* going on, he wondered? One hotel manager being manacled; another unfortunate hotel manager being almost set on fire! Who were these strange fellows he was sharing the lift with, and why were they dressed in vampire fashion? What about Ashley, the chap who chose to dress himself up as a mandarin? What plans had he got in store for the poor wretch who was manager at Laburnum Towers? Why did Ashley take himself around the country causing mayhem and destruction?

All of these vexing questions, and several others, raced through Count Alucard's mind in the short time that it took for the lift to descend from the third floor to ground level – where, before very long, he would learn the answers to them all. . .

"Do you mean to say, Albert, that this hotel is full of magicians?" asked Emily Hollins, gazing out through the car window at the banner which had been hastily strung up above the hotel's entrance.
'LABURNUM TOWERS WELCOMES THE UK MAGICIANS'
"That's right, Emily," said Albert Hollins, fairly glowing with excitement at the prospect of the afternoon ahead. "English magicians, Scottish magicians, Welsh magicians, Irish magicians – and there'll be guest magicians from the continent – even some from America! I'll bet there must be a

120

thousand of them inside the hotel."

"A *thousand*, Dad?" echoed Henry Hollins, glumly, from the back seat of the car which was drawn up outside Laburnum Towers. Having to watch his father's fumbling efforts was bad enough – but the idea of a thousand learner magicians all trying to do their stuff was more than he cared to consider.

"And will they all be doing card tricks, Albert?" asked Emily, voicing Henry's worst fears. "And will they all go wrong, like yours?" she added.

"They're not all beginners, Emily," replied Albert Hollins deciding, for the moment, to ignore his wife's criticism of his own conjuring accomplishments. "Some of them are really famous – you might even have seen them on the telly. This is their annual get-together. Last year they met at Eastbourne, the year before was in Harrogate. You'll enjoy yourselves, believe me."

Emily and Henry Hollins, still unconvinced, raised their eyebrows at each other across the car. This brief exchange did not go unnoticed by Albert Hollins.

"There's going to be a Gala Magic Show on the stage this evening," said Mr Hollins. "There'll be magicians' assistants sawn in half and all kinds of magical happenings. Why don't you two wait in the hotel lobby while I park the car in the car park. Just wait until you get inside," he urged. "It's going to be *fun!*"

Some, at least, of Albert's enthusiasm began to get through to his son.

"Perhaps it *might* be quite exciting, Mum," said

121

Henry as he moved with his mother towards the hotel's entrance. "Just so long as they're not all as bad at magic as dad. Just think – a thousand magicians inside one hotel! Incredible!"

"There's *more* than a thousand folk gathered here this afternoon, young man," said Stanley Groves who had overheard Henry's words as he opened the glass doors at the Hollins's approach. "But they're not all of them magicians, not by any means."

"What are they then?" enquired Emily.

"Laburnum Towers, madam, is the biggest and best conference hotel in the north of England," began the commissionaire proudly, as he tipped his gold-braided cap at Emily Hollins with a white-gloved hand. "There are more than a hundred dog-lovers here today as well – and more than a hundred of our four-legged doggie friends here with them."

"And won't the dogs get under the magicians' feet?" asked Emily.

"Good heavens above!" chuckled Stanley Groves. "I should sincerely hope not, madam. We contrive to keep our separate functions separate, so to speak. The dog show's taking place on the lawn at the back of the hotel. The prizes are being presented by no less a personage than Mr Benny Benson."

"Doesn't he do that TV Quiz Show – *Fancy That!*?" asked Henry.

"That's the gentleman, young man. Then we've got the annual get-together of the UK Magicians – they're far and away the biggest function we've got on today – and they're housed both in the ballroom and the Laburnum Lounge. But we've got several other functions taking place as well."

"Such as?" asked Emily inquisitively.

In answer, the commissionaire gestured at a red baize-covered board which was standing on an easel in the hotel's entrance and on which were listed, in white plastic letters and in alphabetical order, all of that day's events and where they were taking place:

INFORMATION

Aquarium Society AGM	–	Strawberry Salon
Car Boot Sale	–	Hotel Forecourt
Dog Show	–	Lawn/Grounds
Handicrafts Fayre	–	Lilac Loggia
Jigsaw Puzzlers Club	–	Rhododendron Room
UK Magicians	–	Ballroom/Lounge
Whodunnit Club	–	Room 104
All other enquiries	–	Reception Desk

Have A Nice Day!

"My word!" Emily sympathised. "You are rushed off your feet and no mistake!"

"We're used to it," said Stanley Groves with a philosophical shrug of his gold-braided shoulders. "I've known worse. There was one occasion that has gone down in history at Laburnum Towers – a Saturday on which we accommodated fifteen hundred stamp collectors; an All-Comers

123

Invitation Formation Dancing competition – *and* hosted the United Kingdom Tropical Bird championships."

"I'll bet you had your hands full then, and no mistake!" said Emily, her eyes widening at the thought.

"We could have coped with it quite easily, madam – had we been given prior notice that several of our feathered friends of the tropical variety would be uncaged."

"No!"

"As true as I'm standing here." Stanley Groves' face took on a serious expression below his uniform cap. He drew his breath in sharply, and then: "There was this parrot that infiltrated the ballroom, took up a perch in the curtains and would not come down, despite all its owner's pleadings."

"Well!"

"The swear words that parrot launched at those formation dancers do not bear repeating."

"Good gracious me!"

"And then there was the cockateel that made its way into the Rhododendron Room."

"What did it do?"

"You may find this hard to believe, madam, but that wretched bird swooped down and filched a rare, early, unused Lithuanian stamp from out of the very tweezers in a stamp-collector's hand."

Emily Hollins, lost for words, blinked as her mouth dropped open in amazement.

"Nobody has set eyes on that postage stamp, madam, from that day to this."

"Well I'm blessed!" gasped Mrs Hollins,

recovering her powers of speech.

While Stanley Groves and Emily Hollins had been talking, Henry had wandered off across the lobby towards something which had caught his eye.

People were coming and going in all directions across the lobby. Magicians – in all kinds of magicians' costumes – were headed towards, or coming away from, the ballroom or the Laburnum Lounge. Jigsaw Puzzlers were also going to and fro, from the Rhododendron Room to the Candlelight Cafeteria – or vice-versa. There were several people crossing from the entrance towards the lifts to join those already there and waiting to be taken up to the Handicrafts Fayre in the Lilac Loggia on the first floor. In addition to all of which, there was a mass of guests at the reception desk, waiting either to check in, check out, or pose some question to the harrassed receptionists.

But it was none of this that had drawn Henry Hollins' attention. Through the mingling mass of bodies he had spotted something which had caused him to catch his breath. It was a sleek, black, polished coffin, standing upended in a corner of the hotel lobby.

Henry Hollins slipped through the crowded lobby and approached the coffin. He thought he knew the identity of the owner. He also knew how he could be sure of that fact. So as not to draw anyone's attention, he put his back to the coffin, put out a hand behind him and allowed it to slide up the coffin's lid. Yes! Sure enough! His fingers encountered the small brass plate he had expected. The inscription on the plate was worn with the passing of the years and almost indistinguishable to the human eye. But Henry Hollins did not need to look. He knew the legend off by heart.

126

COUNT ALUCARD
The Last Vampire

Henry Hollins' heart thumped hard inside his anorak. He had encountered the exact same coffin on several previous occasions. And one thing was certain, he told himself, as an excited tingle ran right along his spine: where Count Alucard's coffin was to be found, the vegetarian vampire himself could not be far away. He peered in all directions across the busy hotel lobby but the Transylvanian vampire count was nowhere to be seen.

9

"My dear young lady, that really is most incredibly kind of you," said Count Alucard, smiling up at the waitress who had just set down a tempting bowl of fresh fruit salad and a glass of iced tomato juice (spiced with black pepper and Worcester sauce) in the pool of candlelight on the red-checked tablecloth in front of him. "You are extremely gracious, if you will permit me to say so," he added gravely.

"Oh, don't mention it – I'm only doing what I'm paid to do, sir," replied the waitress, slightly flustered and taken aback by the warmth in the Count's words. She was not used to hearing such kind acknowledgements from customers. "Have a nice day!" she said, returning the Count's smile, then turning and moving away to be swallowed up in the half-dark that surrounded all of the cafe's tables.

"One good thing about this place, old chap," the Count observed to himself as he picked up his dessertspoon and then glanced around the dimly-lit Candlelight Cafeteria, "is that a fellow can safely hide himself away for half an hour without fear of being observed."

★　★　★

Some ten minutes or so prior to the above scene, Count Alucard had been standing in the queue at the hotel's reception desk, with Kevin Protheroe and the coffin on the porter's trolley at his side waiting to check out. It was then that he had suffered another disturbing experience. He had seen someone across the lobby whose presence had caused him some concern.

On the previous day, the Transylvanian nobleman had caught no more than a fleeting glimpse of Steven Wilkins, through the taxi window, as the Customs officer had raced out in pursuit of him through the glass doors of the airport arrivals' lounge. On that occasion, the Customs officer had been in uniform – today he was wearing his smart club blazer and the Aquarium Society tie, with the dozens of goldfish embroidered on the dark-blue blackground. But despite the change of clothing, Count Alucard had recognised the Customs officer at once.

Having been forced to spend a lifetime playing a deadly game of hide-and-seek with vampire hunters around the world, the Count had developed a photographic memory for faces.

Even worse though, and only a few seconds later, Count Alucard had spotted a second face he knew. This time it belonged to the Customs officer who had gone through his belongings in the 'Nothing To Declare' channel – and who had asked him all kinds of searching questions. This second Customs officer was also wearing civilian clothing: a brown casual jacket, a pale green shirt, a red-and-green striped tie, beige canvas trousers and a pair of nicely polished brown shoes.

But the very fact that both of the Customs men were out of uniform only served to trouble Count Alucard all the more. It was a sign, he told himself, that his pursuit and capture had grown into an undercover operation.

As he dithered over what to do, the Count suffered yet another shock. His eyes settled upon someone else he had had dealings with the day before. The taxi driver who had brought him to Laburnum Towers had come out of the gentlemen's lavatories and was crossing the hotel lobby. Could it be possible that he was some kind of undercover agent too? It was certainly too much to hope that coincidence was responsible for the three men arriving at the same time in the hotel lobby.

Why – there was probably a plain-clothes Customs officer or police detective skulking behind every potted palm in the hotel! He would have to make himself scarce – and quickly! He did not like leaving his coffin behind – if his pursuers should chance to spot it, it would be obvious that its owner must be near at hand – but it was a risk that had to be taken.

"My dear fellow," the Count began, turning to the hotel porter, "I have suddenly remembered something extremely urgent and requiring my immediate attention – I wonder if I might entrust my luggage into your safekeeping for half an hour or so?"

With which, and without waiting for an answer, Count Alucard pressed a coin into the hotel

130

porter's hand, then ducked his head and made a hasty bee-line across the lobby to seek refuge in the Candlelight Cafeteria. Kevin Protheroe studied the coin in his open palm and wondered – if he added this grubeck to the two which the Count had given him the day before, would he fool the soft-drinks machine in the Games Room into thinking they were ten-pence pieces?

Had Count Alucard been aware of the facts, he would have realised that he had nothing to fear that morning from either Hilton Hargreaves, Steven Wilkins or Monty Wilson. The Customs officers had both forgotten their encounter with Count Alucard on the previous day while the cab driver had not even been aware that he had ferried a Transylvanian vampire in his taxi. As for today, all three of them had personal matters to attend to which were far more exciting than a vampire-hunt.

Steven Wilkins had come to Laburnum Towers to pursue his passion for tropical fish and to meet similarly like-minded folk at the Annual General Meeting of the Aquarium Society. Monty Wilson had stayed at the hotel in order to scour the Car Boot Sale for antique corkscrews to add to his collection. Hilton Hargreaves was there to visit the Handicrafts Fayre where, the shoe shop assistant had informed him, there would be fleecy-lined tartan slippers on sale galore.

Not one of the three therefore spared so much as a passing glance at Count Alucard's coffin as Kevin Protheroe propped it up in a corner of the lobby. Hilton Hargreaves headed hotfoot for the lift which would take him up to the Lilac Loggia;

131

Steven Wilkins strode out purposefully towards the Strawberry Salon, while Monty Wilson crossed the lobby heading briskly for the entrance. As the taxi driver walked out of the hotel towards the forecourt and the Car Boot Sale, he was too preoccupied with thoughts of rare and valuable antique corkscrews to notice his old chum, Stanley Groves, escorting Emily and Henry Hollins into the lobby.

Count Alucard chewed on the succulent slice of peach which he had saved for last from his fresh fruit salad and then tipped his bowl as he dipped his spoon so as not to miss any of the delicious fruit juice lingering in the bottom of the dish.

The Count felt much better for having eaten. He was also more relaxed. He had kept one eye on the cafe's doors while he had been enjoying his meal and had been comforted to note that not one of the three plain-clothes men he had observed in the lobby had followed him into the Candlelight Cafeteria.

Good! Excellent, in fact!

But it would not do, he cautioned himself, to become *too* relaxed. He must not consider himself out of the woods, as it were, until he had put Laburnum Towers well behind him. He peered around the cafeteria but could see nothing save for the pools of candlelight that flickered on every red-checked tablecloth. The faces of the tables' occupants were shrouded in shadow. The very darkness that protected him might also serve to conceal more vampire-hunters lurking at any or every table! But if he *did* have hidden enemies in the cafeteria, would they not have made some sort of move by now? Yes – of course they would! And, if it would not do to become *too* relaxed – neither must he allow anxiety to get the better of him.

The Count sipped at his tall glass of tangy iced tomato juice and tried to calm his jangled nerves.

"Got you!"

Count Alucard's already fluttering heart appeared to leap upwards, into his mouth, at the sound of the voice which rang out just behind his head. Glancing over his shoulder, he was relieved to discover that the lady who had spoken – dressed in motorcyclist's tight-fitting black leathers and carrying a motorcyclist's crash helmet under one arm – was not addressing him. Although she was standing directly behind the Count, her back was turned towards him and she was, in fact, speaking to someone who was hidden from view.

"Hello, Julia," said Ronnie Fairhurst, rather shamefacedly, looking up at his wife. "What are you doing here?"

"I might very well ask you the same question!" snapped Julia Fairhurst. "Sneaking out of the house like that – when you thought I wasn't looking – leaving my new spice-rack lying in pieces all over the kitchen floor! Good gracious me, Ronnie, what on earth came over you?"

"I don't know, Julia," said Ronnie Fairhurst wiggling his shoulders in embarrassment. "Would you like a cup of coffee?" he added in an attempt to change the subject.

"No, Ron, I would *not* like a coffee. And I'll thank you to finish your coffee double-quick so that we can get out of here. You can ride back home on my pillion."

"Very well, dear," said Ronnie Fairhurst meekly, as if resigned to his fate. "But you'll have to wait a minute or two until this coffee cools – otherwise I'll burn my tongue."

"Oh, all right then," said Julia, placing her crash helmet on the table and taking the chair opposite her husband. "But *only* a minute or two mind – don't think you're going to talk me out of taking you home."

"As if I would," said Ronnie Fairhurst with a little sigh. "I know when I'm beaten. Who told you I was in here?"

"I went to the Rhododendron Room. A nice lady in a rose-coloured jumper and a matching cardigan told me to look in here for you."

"Sylvia Cresswell," said Ronnie Fairhurst

nodding his head. "She *is* nice. She's married to Arthur Cresswell – he's the secretary of the Jigsaw Puzzlers Club." He paused, then nodded at his coffee cup and added: "We've broken for coffee."

"So it would seem. Your Mrs Cresswell very kindly offered to let me wait for you in the meeting room. There were coffee and biscuits on the go in there."

"Digestive biscuits, Julia. It was Trevor Hardiman's turn to bring the break-time snacks and he always turns up with digestives, as regular as clockwork." Ronnie Fairhurst paused again and nodded at a selection of fancy biscuits, some of them covered in chocolate, some of them wrapped in inviting gold or silver foil, arranged on a paper doily on a plate next to his cup of coffee. "You know me, Julia," he continued with a little self-conscious smile. "I don't like digestive biscuits – so I thought I'd treat myself in here."

"You always were a faddy person, Ronnie Fairhurst," replied Julia, not too unkindly as she returned his smile and shook her head in mock despair. "If I don't know you now, my lad, I never will."

"I don't suppose . . ." ventured Ronnie Fairhurst, sensing that Julia's temper had cooled and that she might be feeling better disposed towards him. "I don't suppose," he began again, "that you might fancy spending half an hour or so at the Jigsaw Puzzlers Club?"

"*Me?*"

"I could easily put that spice-rack up this evening."

135

"What would I want with the Jigsaw Puzzlers Club?"

"It's more exciting than you think, Julia," said Ronnie Fairhurst and his voice rose with enthusiasm as he continued: "We're trying to beat the UK record for putting a 1500 piece-er together. It's one in the Famous Explorers series: Stanley Meets Doctor Livingstone. Only it's mostly jungle – apart from Stanley and Doctor Livingstone and a couple of native porters carrying Stanley's stuff on a pole." He glanced at his watch. "We're falling behind on our schedule. They'd be more than pleased to let you fit some pieces in – even though you're not a member of the club. 'Many hands make light work', as the saying goes."

"And 'Too many cooks spoil the broth,'" retorted Julia.

"It isn't *just* the club activities, Julia," pleaded Ronnie. "They're a really nice bunch of lads and lasses. You'd like them, once you got to know them. You'd make new friends."

"No, Ronnie," Julia shook her head slowly but firmly. "I'd have nothing at all in common with them. I *hate* jigsaw puzzles," she added in a voice that brooked no argument.

"I know," said Ronnie Fairhurst in hollow tones. He drained his coffee cup. "They'll just have to attempt that UK record without me. Before we go though, Julia – there's one thing that you haven't told me yet?"

"What's that?"

"How did you know that you'd find me at Laburnum Towers?"

"Easy-peasy." Julia Fairhurst unzipped her black leather jacket, felt in the inside pocket, took out a tiny article and laid it on the red-checked tablecloth. "In your haste, you left a valuable clue behind."

"This?" Ronnie Fairhurst picked up the item.

"It was in the middle of the kitchen floor. You must have dropped it."

"But this is a corner bit from Windsor Castle in the Famous Castles series – this has got nothing at all to do with why I'm here today."

"Credit me with some common-sense when it comes to detective work, Ronnie," said Julia as she picked up the corner piece and turned it over in her hand. "I realised when I saw this bit of jigsaw that, wherever you'd disappeared to, it had something to do with jigsaw puzzles. So I looked in the 'Weekend Events' column in this morning's paper. 'Jigsaw Puzzlers Meet Today,' it said, 'at Laburnum Towers'. Mystery solved."

"That was smart of you, Julia," said Ronnie Fairhurst, his eyes opening wide in admiration.

"It was just a matter of putting two-and-two together and coming up with six," said Mrs Fairhurst, modestly. "I pretended I was Sefton Marchbanks. I asked myself what that great detective would have done under such circumstances. The rest was easy. Come along, Ronald," she said, zipping up her leathers, "I'm taking you home . . ."

"Excuse me . . .?"

"Yes?" Julia turned towards the sound of the voice and discovered a young woman with red hair, green eyes and a lot of freckles.

"I hope you'll forgive me for interrupting – but I couldn't help overhearing what you were saying. If I might introduce myself – I'm Police Woman Sandra Simmons . . ."

Count Alucard, who had been pondering over problems of his own, jumped in his chair as the word 'police woman' broke in on his thoughts.

" . . .And these two likely-looking lads," continued Sandra Simmons, indicating two well-built gentlemen who were sharing her table, "are Detective Constable Leslie Archway and Police Sergeant Gordon Threadneedle. . . ."

At this mention of two more members of the police force, not to say their close proximity, Count Alucard glanced over his shoulder with increased agitation. He was all the more disturbed – if not surprised – to discover that the trio of officers were also in plain clothes and therefore, in his estimation, vampire-hunters all three!

Furthermore, Julia Fairhurst, who had previously been standing between her husband and the Count, had moved over towards Sandra Simmons and, for the first time, the Transylvanian nobleman was granted an unhindered view of Ronnie Fairhurst. To add to his dismay, Count Alucard recognised Fairhurst instantly as being yet another of the Customs men who had pursued him through the airport on the previous day.

The net, it seemed, was suddenly closing in. . .

Arriving at a sudden decision, and deciding that his only hope lay in throwing caution to the winds, Count Alucard leaped to his feet and took to the

138

heels of his well-polished shoes. His long black cloak spread out behind him as on his gangly legs, he sprinted towards the doors which led to the lobby.

Policewoman Sandra Simmons, her two colleagues and Mr and Mrs Fairhurst had watched, puzzled, as the tall, thin black-garbed figure had taken off at speed and now disappeared into the body of the hotel.

"Well!" said Sandra Simmons. "What on earth do you imagine all that was about?"

"Search me!" gasped Detective Constable Leslie Archway.

"I haven't got a clue!" murmured Police Sergeant Gordon Threadneedle as he scratched his head.

And both Julia and Ronnie Fairhurst blinked and raised their eyebrows signifying that they were also puzzled by the customer's odd behaviour.

139

Under normal circumstances, of course, both Customs Officer Fairhurst and Policewoman Simmons would have remembered that their respective paths had crossed with the vampire's the day before – while Sergeant Threadneedle and Constable Archway would, without doubt, have reminded themselves about the official warning regarding the monster which had been broadcast only a few hours before. But these were no ordinary circumstances – today was Saturday, they were all off-duty and their thoughts were fixed on more important matters.

"What was it you were about to say," began Julia Fairhurst, turning back to Sandra Simmons, "before that funny-looking gentleman ran across the room?"

"Oh yes!" replied the policewoman. "I couldn't help overhearing you mention Sefton Marchbanks. Forgive me for prying into your private life – but are you a fan of that famous fictional detective?"

"I'll say I am!" said Julia. "I've read every one of the Marchbanks books – well, every one except the latest one, *The Corpse On The Colonel's Carpet*, I haven't been able to get hold of a copy of that one yet."

"I have," said Sergeant Threadneedle with enthusiasm. "It's the best one yet. I couldn't put it down. I sat up in bed until two o'clock in the morning. My wife was going crackers."

"Ooooh!" went Julia as she sucked in her cheeks with excitement at the prospect of the pleasure she had in store.

"We three," said Sandra Simmons, nodding at

her fellow officers, "are members of The Whodunnit Club."

"I've never heard of that," said Julia Fairhurst.

"Not many people have," said Leslie Archway glumly.

"That's probably why there's just the three of us left," added Gordon Threadneedle with a sigh.

"We used to have quite a good turn-out," said Sandra Simmons. "Then one lady left to have a baby and a couple of gentlemen went off together and took up golf. We did have an assistant bank manager member who was *very* keen – but he got transferred to Aberdeen. So – what with one thing and another . . ." Sandra's voice faltered and her shoulders drooped.

"But what does The Whodunnit Club do?" asked Julia.

"It meets here every second Saturday in the month," said Gordon Threadneedle.

"We used to meet in the Rosewood Room – it's got its own coffee machine and the hotel used to lay on bourbon biscuits," said Leslie Archway. "But now that there's only the three of us, we meet in Room 104 and come down here for coffee."

"Still, looking on the bright side – we have some very enjoyable meetings," said Sandra Simmons stoutly. "We talk about the latest detective books, swap books that we've read, and take it in turns to give little talks about our favourite authors."

"It sounds great," said Julia, with genuine enthusiasm. "Right up my street in fact."

"That's what I was thinking," ventured Sandra. "When I heard you mention Sefton Marchbanks,

I wondered whether you might fancy coming to our meeting this afternoon?"

"Sefton Marchbanks is our subject for today," said Leslie Archway.

"Never!" Julia caught her breath with amazement. "Well – what a coincidence!" she added with a gulp.

"So – what do you think?" asked Gordon Threadneedle. "Would you care to join us?"

Julia Fairhurst, undecided, gnawed pensively at her lower lip as she remembered the spice-rack which was lying in pieces on her kitchen floor.

"Why don't you, Julia?" urged Ronnie, thinking about the part-completed 1500 piece Stanley Meets Doctor Livingstone in the Rhododendron Room. With luck, he might still be able to play his part in the Jigsaw Puzzle Club's race against time. "You go to The Whodunnit Club and I'll go back to my jigsaw puzzle chums. We'll meet back here after both our meetings finish."

"Well. . . ."

"Like I said before, Julia," began Ronnie, reading his wife's thoughts. "I can easily finish the spice-rack when we get home this evening."

"Oh – bubbles to the spice-rack!" Julia Fairhurst had arrived at a decision. A broad grin spread across her face as she looked at the three members of The Whodunnit Club who were smiling back. "What are we waiting for?" she said.

Hurtling out of the Candlelight Cafeteria, Count Alucard had come to a sudden stop, his shiny black

142

shoes skidding on the lobby floor. Not one of the vampire-hunters appeared to be on his immediate heels and he might do well to proceed with caution, he told himself.

Glancing across the lobby, he caught sight of a door which stood invitingly open. Trying to look unconcerned, the Count strolled over and stepped through the open door into the empty lift. Before anyone could make a move to join him, Count Alucard reached out and jabbed at the first button which met his thumb. The door closed silently and the lift began to ascend.

Thankful for the few peaceful moments, Count Alucard heaved a sigh of relief and peered into the mirror on the back wall of the lift. It reassured him to be able to see behind himself and to know that no-one was looking over his shoulder.

Looking into the mirror, the lift was empty. If the mirror was to be believed, of course – he was not even there himself!

10

"My goodness me!" said Albert Hollins, standing in the ballroom doorway and beaming at the sight that met his eyes. Then, turning to his wife and son, he added: "What have you got to say *now*?"

"Well I never!" were the words that Emily chose to suit the occasion.

Henry Hollins blinked, twice, but kept his silence – an indication, perhaps, that he was too overawed to speak.

Because of all the events that were happening at Laburnum Towers on that Saturday, it had taken Mr Hollins quite some time to find a space in the hotel's car park. Emily and Henry had been forced to kick their heels in the lobby while they waited for Albert to join them. When he had finally arrived, had eventually run to earth the magic convention tickets in an inside pocket, and had at last escorted Emily and Henry into the ballroom, first impressions suggested that the occasion might prove well worth the waiting time that they had had to suffer.

The ballroom, which was reserved for Laburnum Towers most important functions, was the biggest and grandest space the hotel was proud to possess.

The ornate plaster-work on its pale-green walls was picked out with gold paint and the high, arched ceiling was hung with a dozen and more many-branched cut-glass chandeliers.

But it was neither the sheer size of the ballroom nor the glittering elegance of its fittings that had brought about Mr and Mrs Hollinses' admiration. It was what was going on inside the room that had caused the pair to gasp.

The Laburnum Towers ballroom was fairly bursting with things to do with magic. Some fifty or so stalls had been set up along the length of the ballroom, in three rows, creating a sort of indoor market. Each and every one of the stalls was manned by magical dealers, demonstrating and selling all kinds of magic goods.

There was every conceivable kind of trick on offer. There were card-tricks; rope-tricks; coin-tricks; tricks with watches; tricks with wallets; paper-tearing tricks and tricks with colourful big silk handkerchiefs. There were tricks with large gleaming chromium-plated rings which magically joined themselves together and tricks with mysterious balls, decorated with moons and stars, that *looked* solid enough, but which floated magically in the air. There were cunning tricks with little velvet bags, that caused objects to appear, and tricks with ingeniously made wooden boxes which caused things to vanish magically.

There were tricks on sale of every shape and size – ranging from tricks that would slip easily inside a schoolgirl's or a schoolboy's pocket up to large, impressive stage-size illusions.

And each and every one of the stalls was thronged with magicians eager to exchange their money for goods which would serve to add to their magical skills. There were amateur magicians, professional magicians, lady magicians, old magicians, young magicians – some of them no older than Henry Hollins himself.

Indeed, had Henry not had his mind on more important matters, he might easily have been tempted into splurging out his pocket money on one, at least, of the intriguing pocket tricks.

But Henry Hollins was still wondering as to the whereabouts of Count Alucard. Having spotted the Count's very own coffin in the lobby, Henry would not be satisfied until he had located his old chum. What made matters worse, was that so many of the magicians were wearing suits so similar to the one worn by his friend, that Henry kept thinking he could see the Count at every stall.

The magical convention had opened its doors several hours earlier and most of the magicians were clutching bulging plastic bags containing the tricks they had bought so far. Those magicians who, like Albert Hollins, had brought their wives along with them, it could be noted, did not have plastic bags which bulged quite so much as those carried by magicians who had come unaccompanied.

"Don't overdo it, Albert," said Emily nervously, echoing the sentiments of the other magicians' wives, as she saw her husband head towards an enticing stall, eager to hand over the money he was already clutching in his fist. "Don't go *too* mad," added Emily forlornly.

But Albert Hollins had the gleam of the hobbyist in his eye. He felt that he had some quick buying to attend to if he was going to catch up with his fellow-magicians, who were also scrambling to get rid of their cash.

"I'll see you later, Mum," said Henry, snatching the opportunity to move away from his parents.

"Don't stray too far, Henry," said Emily, glancing back at her son.

"If we lose each other in these crowds, we'll meet up in the cafe in half an hour," called Albert Hollins over his shoulder as he jostled with several other magicians, all doing their best to spend rather a lot of money on a rather small card trick.

Henry Hollins, having gained half an hour's breathing space in which to find the Count, headed through the crush towards the doors leading to the lobby.

Count Alucard, having got out of the lift at the second floor, had walked the length of several bedroom corridors which, thankfully, were all deserted, before arriving at a flight of narrow stairs marked by a sign which read: 'STAFF ONLY'. The staircase would, he guessed, take him down to the hotel's back entrance.

Count Alucard had had more than enough of Laburnum Towers. If only he could manage to slip out quietly at the back, he told himself, it would suit him admirably. He could then make his way through the bushes, skirting the drive, as far as the

147

main road where, with luck, he should be able to pick up a passing taxi. Sadly, it would mean abandoning his precious coffin, at least for the time being. But, if everything went to plan, once things had quietened down and he had established himself in new lodgings in some quiet backwater, he could call back for his luggage in a day or two or, better still, arrange for his things to be sent on to him.

Encountering no-one on his way down the stairs, save for a young chambermaid with her arms full of dirty linen who gave him not so much as a passing glance, the Count arrived at ground level. Ahead of him, at the end of yet another long corridor, he saw a double-door marked 'PUSH TO EXIT'. Delighted that, after all of his previous setbacks he was able to make such an easy escape, Count Alucard set off towards the safety-exit.

"It is my great pleasure to announce that the first prize for the Most Obedient Dog in this show . . ." said Benny Benson, the famous TV quiz show presenter, pausing teasingly before revealing the winner's name.

On the grass, in front of the judges' stand, the proud owners of the four finalists in the Most Obedient Dog category held their breath, their dogs sitting in obedient silence by their feet.

" . . .Wait for it . . .!" added Benny Benson, keeping the finalist dog owners in even more suspense as he wiggled his eyebrows at his audience in the well-rehearsed way that had made him famous with TV viewers throughout the land.

"Oh, do get a move on, you silly man!" muttered Granville Cazelot to himself.

The Customs chief was one of the lucky owners who had made it to the final four. He glanced down anxiously at Wolf who, for the moment, was sitting quite still on his haunches and on his best behaviour. But Granville Cazelot knew full well that the longer that Benny Benson waffled on, the more likely it became that his German Shepherd dog might bark again, or fidget, or otherwise let him down. Cazelot turned his gaze on Police Inspector Archie Oliver who was standing next to him and whose poodle, Trixiebelle the Third, was also one of the chosen few.

"Good luck, Archie," said Cazelot through gritted teeth.

"*Bon chance*, Granville," replied Oliver, but the words did not come easily.

The two men smiled sourly at each other. Although they had known one another for a great many years, and had attended many doggie events together, they had never before been finalists in the same event and the circumstance was proving a severe strain on their friendship.

"If that pampered, powdered poodle takes first prize," the Customs officer told himself, "it'll be a travesty of justice."

"If that great hulking ugly Alsatian wins the category, in preference to my Trixiebelle," Archie Oliver said to himself, "it'll mean that there's been some sort of fiddle."

"Right you are then, lads and lasses!" cried Benny Benson, wiggling his eyebrows yet again. "I

149

won't keep you in suspense a moment longer – the first prize for the Most Obedient Dog goes to . . ."

But the host of TV's *Fancy That!* did not manage to finish his sentence. At the very moment that he had begun to speak, a loud "CLANG!" had rung out behind his back. The sound had been caused by the slamming shut of the self-locking exit-doors behind the gangling, black-cloaked, pale-complexioned man who had come out of the hotel.

In his anxiety to flee from Laburnum Towers, Count Alucard had quite forgotten about the dog show on the hotel's rear lawn. He stood motionless for several moments, as though transfixed, as the hundred or so show dogs took their lead from Benny Benson and stared across in his direction, heads cocked, ears pricked and panting with excitement.

"Ah-Whooo-OOO-oooOOOH . . .!" went Wolf, the German Shepherd dog, breaking an awesome silence.

If there had been any doubts in the Count's mind that the German Shepherd, because of its close relationship with the wolf, had some sort of affinity with his vampire self, they were soon dispelled.

The big German Shepherd dog leaped to its feet and set off, at speed, towards the Transylvanian count.

"Wolf!" cried Granville Cazelot, seeing his chances of taking the first prize for owning the Most Obedient Dog in the show fading fast.

But if the German Shepherd had heard his master's voice, he had no intention whatsoever of obeying it. Tongue lolling and the fur standing up all along his spine, Wolf made a bee-line for Count Alucard – and heaven save anything that stood in his path.

Unfortunately for Benny Benson, in front of the microphone and up on the judges' platform, he chanced to be the only object in direct line between the German Shepherd and the Count. As Wolf launched himself into a leap intended to carry him over the platform, his front paws struck the TV presenter full on the chest, hard, sending him sprawling onto his back struggling to hold his hairpiece on.

"Wolf! Wolf! Be told! Heel! HEEL!" yelled the Customs chief, fearing that the dog's outrageous behaviour could lead to both his pet *and* himself being banned from competition for all time.

But Granville Cazelot's German Shepherd dog was not the only canine to disgrace itself that afternoon – far from it!

"Yelp! Yelp! Yelp . . .!"

Taking her cue from Wolf, Police Inspector Archie Oliver's poodle, Trixiebelle the Third, was also quickly up onto her manicured paws and bounding along in the Count's direction, in full throttle and shedding talcum powder in her wake.

"*Bad*, girl! *Bad*, dog!" shouted Archie Oliver after his fast-fleeing poodle. "Naughty! Naughty! Sit, girl! SIT!"

"Ah-ruff! Ah-RUFF . . .!"

"Will yez pack that in, O'Flaherty, and come back here this instant else yez'll be in a divvil of a lot of trouble!" bellowed the lady owner of the Irish wolfhound which had also been on the short list

151

for the Most Obedient Dog award, but was now hard on the heels of Wolf and Trixiebelle the Third.

"!Grrrr! Grrrr . . .!" "Woof-WOOF . . .!" "Yap! Yap! Yap-YAP . . .!"

In twos-and-threes and then in fours-and-fives, all of the dogs in the show, impervious to their owners despairing pleas, leaped to their paws and set off, yapping, yelping and barking, across the well-trimmed lawn, bounding over the raised platform where Benny Benson lay helpless and hairless, then on towards the black-garbed figure locked outside the hotel's back fire-exit.

The Count, seeing a hundred dogs and more hurtling straight towards him, found movement in his frozen limbs at last and took off on his long legs, along the back of the hotel.

The hundred dogs – all shapes and sizes, some of them brown, some black, some white, some spotted and some brindled – checked in their various lengths of stride (some long, some short) and changed direction, still hot in pursuit of the sprinting sprightly figure with his black cloak billowing out behind him.

"It's *him*, Archie!" cried Granville Cazelot, his voice rising in incredulous horror. "It's that ruddy vampire!"

As the Customs chief had watched the pack of dogs take off after the fleeing man, the pieces had finally fallen into place inside his head. The running man fitted, exactly, the description of the missing monster which Granville Cazelot had been given the day before: 'Black suit; white frilly-fronted shirt; white bow tie and long, crimson-

lined cloak'. There could be no doubt whatsoever as to the rogue's identity.

"By golly gumbo, Cazzo – you're right!" gasped Police Inspector Archie Oliver, who also had the vampire's description committed to memory.

"Get after him – all of you!" yelled the Customs chief, attempting to egg on his fellow dog owners with wild, overarm sweeping gestures.

"Tally-ho!" cried Archie Oliver, setting a good example by setting off in chase himself.

One by one, the dog owners responded and started out in ragged, unenthusiastic file in pursuit of the rangy black-garbed figure and the following canine pack. And, if most of the dog owners were more concerned with recapturing their errant pets than with tackling a blood-drinking monster – well, who could blame them . . .?

The Car Boot Sale on the forecourt at Laburnum Towers was not proving the runaway success that its organisers had hoped for.

Apart from the vehicles' owners, there were only some half-dozen or so prospective customers examining the car-boots' contents when Count Alucard appeared around the hotel's corner, pursued by the string of excited, yelping dogs and headed straight for the two lines of cars.

The car-boot salesmen and their customers had seen the advancing canine charge in sufficient time to leap out of its path – with one exception.

Monty Wilson, the antique-corkscrew collector cab driver, was bending down and peering at the rusty items of junk that lay at the bottom of the boot of an ancient, battered Ford Popular. Intent on this task, Monty did not hear the warning shouts of his fellow customers. Chancing to glance up at the very last moment, he was horrified to see the wild-eyed Count Alucard only several metres away and headed straight towards him and – more to the point – the rag-tag canine army close behind the Count, scattering anything and everything in its path.

Wolf, the German Shepherd dog, and O'Flaherty, the Irish wolfhound, had been overtaken now by Billy Bonzo, a lean-limbed taut-muscled greyhound, with Trixiebelle the Third having dropped back into a middle group of terriers, setters and spaniels. Ching-Ching and Wan-Toon, the two Pekingese, were bringing up the rear in company with Hermann, a German dachshund.

Seizing the only avenue of escape from the advancing horde, Monty Wilson leaped inside the Ford Popular's boot and pulled the lid down smartly on himself.

Just in time. A split-second later, his black cloak spread out behind him, Count Alucard sprinted past, closely followed by the tightly bunched leading dogs – several of whom left their paw-marks on car bonnets and even car roofs as they strove to catch up with the Count. Trestle tables were upturned, sending small pottery pieces crashing to the ground while other sturdier items rolled underneath parked vehicles.

Then, as quickly as they had come, both the

Count and the dogs were gone. A moment later, Police Inspector Oliver, Chief Customs Officer Cazelot and several of the fittest dog owners led the pursuit around the corner of the hotel.

"They went that way!" shouted the owner of the Ford Popular, a heavily-built man, called Eric Wilmslow, who was wearing a knitted diamond-patterned pullover over a grubby string vest.

Lacking the breath to reply, the chasing group of humans followed the direction of Eric's pointing finger and, in seconds, they too were out of sight.

"Help! Help! *Please*, help!" Monty Wilson's muffled cries came from the Ford Popular's boot.

"Are you all right, matey?" asked Eric as he swung the boot-lid open.

Monty Wilson made no reply as he hauled himself up onto his knees inside the boot. Whilst crouching fearfully in the dark, his fingers had closed around an object in the junk on the floor. Now, glancing down, he was astonished to discover that he was clutching a mid-nineteenth century corkscrew fashioned in the shape of the past prime minister, Benjamin Disraeli. It was a rare collector's item for which the cab driver had been searching for many years.

"How much do you want for this?" he asked Eric, trying hard not to show his excitement.

Eric slipped a hand inside his string-vest and scratched at his armpit thoughtfully as he pondered how much he dare ask for what he considered to be a worthless bit of rubbish?

11

With the Car Boot Sale lying wrecked behind him, Count Alucard had been forced into making a quick decision. Either he could continue running along the hotel's gravel driveway, which led towards the main road and freedom – or else he could turn right and go back into Laburnum Towers from which he had only recently made his escape.

Considering his circumstances, it did not take the Count long to make up his mind. What sort of a figure would he present, he asked himself, charging along a main road with a hundred dogs, and more besides, in hot pursuit? And also, if he chose to take that route, how long could he hope to remain at large before the dogs, or the police, or the Customs men, or the vampire-hunters – or, indeed, all four of these groups together – should catch up with him?

No, there was only one thing to be done. Without faltering in his long-legged stride, Count Alucard had veered right and barged through the entrance doors back into Laburnum Towers.

In doing this, the Count had reckoned upon the army of dogs being held back outside by the plate-glass double-doors. No such luck. By sheer weight of numbers and canine paw-power, the dogs had little difficulty in pushing open both glass doors.

They surged into the entrance lobby en masse, bowling over Stanley Groves, the uniformed commissionaire, as he rushed forward in an attempt to hold them back. The commissionaire fell back, gold braid and all, into a potted palm as the canine army poured into the lobby. Then, instead of bringing down the Count, they pressed forward, surrounding him and jostling against each other as each one attempted to rub its fur against his legs.

All at once, the truth became clear to the Count. The dogs had not been chasing him with a view to bringing him to the ground – like the big German Shepherd dog that was always at their forefront, they were all – each and every one – anxious to be his friends. It seemed that the unique and close relationship which he enjoyed with the wolf-pack in the Forest of Tolokovin also held good with every single one of these dogs.

They wished to help not hinder him. They were happy to run wherever he ran. They wanted to share the pleasure of his company.

Even so, the Count told himself, he would still need to act quickly if he was to evade the clutches of the chasing pack of humans who, at any second, were about to burst into the hotel. Glancing urgently around the lobby, he spotted an arched corridor leading he knew not where.

"*Shrubza vora shrucka glott!*" the Count murmured to himself, that being the Transylvanian equivalent of the English proverb: 'Any port in a storm'. And, so saying, he took off along the corridor with the rabble army of dogs bounding along in front, beside and at back of him, almost succeeding unintentionally in tripping him up.

Inside the Rhododendron Room, with one eye always on the clock, the eighteen members of the Jigsaw Puzzlers Club, grouped around the central table, strove to finish the 1500 piece Stanley Meets Doctor Livingstone. There was less than an hour to go. They had completed all four sides of the puzzle and filled in most of the difficult jungle bits – all that remained were the figures of the two famous men and the native bearers.

When the puzzle was completed, Arthur Cresswell, the club secretary, was going to give the membership a talk which he had titled: 'Animals And Their Place In Jigsaw Puzzles'. To make his lecture all the more interesting, Arthur Cresswell had brought along the packing-case full of jigsaw puzzles all of which had animals for their subject-matter. Before the meeting had begun, Mr and Mrs Cresswell had stacked up the 'Animal Jigsaw' boxes, like a supermarket display, at one end of the Rhododendron Room.

First though, there was a world record waiting to be won. It lay within the Jigsaw Puzzlers' grasp.

"We're going to do it, too," muttered Ronnie Fairhurst to himself, his brow creased with concentration, as he slotted home another bit of jungle greenery.

It was at this moment that the swing-door at one end of the room burst open and the leading dog, Billy Bonzo, hurtled in with Wolf, the German Shepherd dog at his heels.

In less time than it takes a dog to bark, the Rhododendron Room was alive with dogs of every size, shape, breed and colour, turning, twisting and leaping over each other. It had not been Count Alucard's intention to disturb the Jigsaw Puzzlers Club – he had been borne helplessly along on the furry four-legged tide.

Luckily, the dog invasion did not last long. In a matter of seconds, or even less, the dogs had discovered a second swing-door at the opposite end of the Rhododendron Room. They were on their way, as quickly as they had come, still carrying the black-cloaked vampire count along in their midst – and leaving a trail of devastation behind.

The central table, containing the almost-completed Famous Explorers puzzle, had been upended by Sommersby, a lumbering St Bernard, ably assisted by Natasha and Nerissa, a couple of silky-coated borzois. The pyramid of jigsaw puzzle boxes had been sent flying by the concerted efforts of Trueman, the Yorkshire terrier, and Winston, the bulldog – not forgetting the assistance of a couple of highly-strung spaniels.

All of the bits from the animals jigsaw puzzle boxes were mixed up with the bits belonging to Stanley Meets Doctor Livingstone and spread all across the floor.

"Oh, dear!" said Sylvia Cresswell, giving voice to the views of all the Jigsaw Club members who seemed to have been struck dumb by the invasion.

"This is going to take some sorting out and no mistake!" said Arthur Cresswell, gravely surveying the 30,000 jumbled-up bits of different puzzles.

"Forgive our barging in like this," panted Police Inspector Oliver, as he led the chasing band of humans, which now numbered a couple of angry

Car Boot Sale people among its ranks, into the Rhododendron Room. "But did a tall, thin man in a long black cloak and a lot of dogs come through here, by any chance?"

"Fairhurst!" gasped Granville Cazelot, surprised at finding one of his own underlings in the hotel. "Have you let that monster get past you yet again?"

Ronnie Fairhurst, with no excuse to offer, could only nod his head.

Steven Wilkins, the tropical fish-fancying Customs officer, had been leaning back with his chair balanced on two legs, sucking at the end of his ballpoint pen and staring up at the strawberry-coloured ceiling when the horde of dogs, still bearing Count Alucard in its midst, burst in through the swing-door which led from the Rhododendron Room to the Strawberry Salon.

Up until that very moment, Stevie's Saturday had not been proving half as enjoyable as he had hoped.

For a start, the Aquarium Society's Annual General Meeting had been a dull event concerned with facts and figures – the Auditor's Accounts and the Treasurer's Report – without so much as a mention of a living tropical fish. Even worse, when the AGM had ended, about half an hour previously, the guest speaker who had been booked proved to be as boring as the events which had preceded him. Roger Carslake-Whittingbury, a serious-looking gentleman wearing a sports jacket with leather patches on the elbows, had a voice which droned on, and on and on, without ever a change of tone.

Worst of all though, proved to be the subject he had chosen: My Hobby. Neither Stevie Wilkins nor, in fact, most of the members present were able to believe their ears when Roger Carslake-Whittingbury announced that *his* hobby was stamp collecting! A murmur of disgust had travelled around the Strawberry Salon when Carslake-Whittingbury made this fact known. One veteran member was heard to whisper to his neighbour that he intended to raise the matter of this choice of speaker at *next* year's AGM.

On that particular Saturday though, the Aquarium Society's membership, fish-fanciers all, had no choice except to sit slumped in their chairs while Carslake-Whittingbury wittered on in his boring voice about penny blacks, two-penny reds and first day covers.

The onslaught then of the hundred odd dogs and the man-in-black into the meeting had proved a welcome diversion for the majority of the members.

For one thing, there was little damage that the dogs could effect in the Strawberry Salon. There were no jigsaw puzzle pieces to be spilled out of their boxes. There were no attempts at world records to be interrupted. All that the Strawberry Salon contained, apart from the guest speaker, were the Aquarium Society's officers and members, the fitted furniture and the plastic chairs those present were sitting on.

As the canine army whirlwinded into the Salon,

the society's members all leaped to safety on the shelf-table which ran right around the walls. The dogs overturned all of the plastic chairs, of course, but no other harm was done. As soon as the milling dogs had managed to locate the door at the opposite end of the salon, they had pushed it open and made their exit, still carrying the Count along with them.

The incident had proved such an entertainment after the guest-speaker's efforts, that several of the members, still perched on the shelf-table managed to rouse a ragged cheer as the last three dogs, Ching-Ching, Wan-Toon and Hermann scampered from the room.

Steven Wilkins did not join in with these minor celebrations. Something had attracted his attention. From where he was standing on the shelf-table, being a tallish man, he was able to peer over the top of a fitted cupboard which did not look as if it had seen a duster for years and years. Reaching across, he tugged at the tiny oblong bit of paper that had somehow got lodged between the cupboard and the wall and had caught his eye.

"May I see that?" said a voice at Wilkins' shoulder.

The Customs officer turned to discover that standing next to him was Roger Carslake-Whittingbury who was holding out a hand.

"Certainly – be my guest," said Stevie Wilkins as he handed the guest-speaker the tiny scrap of paper.

Roger Carslake-Whittingbury gave a little shiver of excitement and let out a long, low whistle.

"What is it?" asked Wilkins.

"Believe me or believe me not, my friend," began Carslake-Whittingbury and his usually boring voice was now bursting with enthusiasm, "but what you have here is a rare and valuable early unused Lithuanian postage stamp."

"Is it really?"

"If memory serves me correct, this stamp was filched out of a stamp-dealer's tweezers by a cockateel during a stamp-collectors' convention here some years ago – the wretched bird must have secreted it on top of that cupboard."

"Well I'm blowed!"

"You're a very fortunate fellow," said Roger Carslake-Whittingbury handing the stamp carefully back to Stevie Wilkins. "When it's delivered back to its rightful owner you could be in for quite a substantial reward."

Steven Wilkins blinked in surprise. He was beginning to think that perhaps stamp-collecting wasn't such a dull hobby after all. . . .

It was at that moment that the door to the Strawberry Salon burst open for a second time. Granville Cazelot, Archie Oliver and their recruits bustled into the room.

"Attention, please!" snapped the Customs chief to the members of the Aquarium Society who, for the most part, were still standing on the wooden shelf. "Sorry to interrupt your meeting, but we're hot on the trail of a lot of dogs, they didn't by any chance. . . ." He broke off as he spotted Stevie Wilkins up on the shelf. "Wilkins! Are you here as well? What are you doing up there, lad?"

"Getting down, sir," replied the Customs man, daring the joke as he was off-duty and out of uniform.

"You can cut out the funny stuff, Wilkins!" barked Granville Cazelot. "The blood-drinking monster that you allowed to slip through your fingers at the airport yesterday is at large in this hotel."

"The dogs are on his trail though," added Archie Oliver. "We're following the dogs."

"They went that way, sir," said Wilkins, pointing to the door at the other end of the room. "Only a moment or so ago – what's more, now that I come to think about it, that vampire was with them."

"In which case, there is not a moment to be lost." The Customs chief paused and allowed his eyes to wander over the aquarists as they clambered down on to the strawberry-leaf patterned carpet. "If any of you gentlemen would care to join us, your assistance would be much appreciated. This is a vampire-hunt!"

Tumbling out of the Strawberry Salon in leaps and bounds, barking and yelping, with Wolf, Billy Bonzo and Dolly, a slightly dotty dalmatian, now vying for the lead, the dogs paused, bewildered for a moment, as they wondered whether to turn right, which would have taken them back into the lobby, or left, which would have led them towards the rear of the hotel.

The moment of indecision was sufficient time for Count Alucard to untangle his spindly legs from the main body of the pack and take command of the situation himself.

"This way, my darlings!" cried the Count, choosing to go neither right nor left but straight ahead and up a flight of sweeping stairs which led, according to a cardboard hand-written sign, to the first floor Lilac Loggia and the Handicrafts Fayre.

But if Count Alucard's and the dog-pack's recent intrusion into the Strawberry Salon had proved a stroke of luck for Stevie Wilkins, their invasion of the Handicrafts Fayre was to result in nothing short of a disaster so far as Hilton Hargreaves was concerned.

Hilton Hargreaves had just found what he had been looking for the whole of that day – a pair of fleecy-lined tartan slippers which fitted him perfectly! When Rita Oliver, the Saturday shoe shop assistant had told the Customs officer that he might find a pair of slippers to suit him at Laburnum Towers, she had spoken the truth.

There were lots of other stalls, of course, positioned along the first floor loggia – a balconied gallery which overlooked the lobby – selling hand-knitted toys, locally hand-crafted jewellery, home-baked cakes, home-made chutney and a score of other things besides. But it was the stall that was selling slippers that had brought sheer delight to Hilton Hargreaves.

But as so often happens, alas, his moment of pure joy turned in an instant into bitter tragedy.

Hilton Hargreaves had barely laid hold of the slippers he had spent so long seeking, when Count Alucard's long-limbed frame came leaping over the top of the stairs. If the Count could have changed direction then, he would have done so all too happily. But there was no other way to go except along the balcony through the Handicrafts Fayre.

Hargreaves recognised the newcomer at once but things happened then so quickly there was nothing that the Customs officer could do. The host of ill-assorted pedigree dogs followed close on Count Alucard's heels and pandemonium ensued. Again, the Count and the eager army of dogs had come and gone in seconds – but the damage that they left behind was awesome to behold.

Hand-knitted cuddly figures lay in curious broken attitudes all over the loggia. There were odd slippers everywhere. Smashed pots of chutney spread their greeny-yellowy mess across the floor. Sponge cakes and Swiss rolls had crumbled where they fell and were fast being trod unintentionally into the carpet by the bewildered stall-attendants and the dazed shoppers. A shower of cheap earrings and cuff-links had shot over the balcony and cascaded onto the lobby below.

When Granville Cazelot, Archie Oliver, Stevie Wilkins, Ronnie Fairhurst, the dog owners, the Car Boot Sale persons, the Jigsaw Puzzlers and the recently recruited members from the Aquarium Society arrived on the loggia, there was no need for them to enquire if Count Alucard and the dogs had passed that way. Events spoke for themselves.

"You too, Hargreaves?" Granville Cazelot's eyebrows rose in surprise as he discovered yet another member of his staff in the hotel. "Couldn't *you* have made some attempt to halt the monster's progress?"

"Sorry, sir," said Hargreaves, giving an embarrassed little shrug. "It all happened so quickly – and at the time I was. . . ."

"Never mind the excuse, Hargreaves!" broke in the Customs chief. "Fall in behind the others and let's get after it – we're wasting more time."

"But, chief. . . ."

"No 'buts', laddie!" snapped Cazelot, setting off again in the direction taken by the quarry. "Just do as you're told."

"Yes, sir."

Hilton Hargreaves had been trying on his new slippers for size and comfort when the dogs had poured along the loggia. Now, for the second time in as many days, he was forced to set off in pursuit of a vampire with slippers on his feet.

"There was a dark, ominous stain in the very centre of the Indian carpet. The famous detective knelt down

169

and prodded at the mark with his forefinger. It did not surprise him to discover that the stain was still wet.

" 'Just as I suspected,' the great man murmured to himself. 'This proves without a shadow of a doubt that Commander Fortescue was murdered here, in the morning room, and his dead body was dragged into the conservatory, where it was found.' "

Julia Fairhurst, who was reading aloud the passage from *The Corpse On The Colonel's Carpet*, the latest Sefton Marchbanks murder mystery, which she had finally managed to get hold of to the members of The Whodunnit Club, paused for dramatic effect.

"I think I've guessed who the murderer is already," said Leslie Archway with some self-satisfaction.

"I thought I knew who the murderer was, Leslie, when I first read the book," cautioned Gordon Threadneedle, who had brought the book along. "But when I got to the last chapter, I found out that I was wrong."

"Go on, Julia," said Sandra Simmons encouragingly. "Read some more – I'm enjoying it."

Julia Fairhurst, who was enjoying her introductory meeting of The Whodunnit Club, glanced down at the page and began to read again:

"But Sefton Marchbanks was too intent on his investigations to realise that, behind his back, the handle of the door to the morning room was being turned gently from outside. Slowly, the door began to open. . . ."

Julia Fairhurst broke off with a gulp. But this

time she had not paused for dramatic effect. Out of the corner of her eye, Julia had noticed that the handle on the door of Room 104 was also turning slowly – exactly like the one in the novel she was reading!

Julia Fairhurst gulped again. Sandra, Gordon and Leslie followed Julia's glance as the door began to open. A pale-faced man with sad, red-rimmed eyes peered into the room.

"Do forgive me," said Count Alucard. "I am most dreadfully sorry – I didn't realise the room was occupied. I was. . ."

Count Alucard was not allowed to finish the sentence. The army of dogs which was fast assembling around his legs in the corridor took matters into their own paws and began scratching and pushing with their combined weights at the door to Room 104. Count Alucard lost his grip on the door which suddenly burst open.

The members of The Whodunnit Club watched in wide-eyed astonishment as dogs of all shapes and breeds and sizes, some of the smaller ones scrambling over the bigger ones that had preceded them, poured into the room. Again, Count Alucard was swept along on the canine tide.

Room 104 was nowhere near large enough to contain the avalanche of dogs. The larger dogs, led by Wolf, Billy Bonzo and Sommersby, the St Bernard, being first to barge their way through the door, were also the first to realise not only that the room was not big enough to hold the horde of dogs piling in behind them, but also that there was no other exit. Realising the danger, the front dogs

171

turned and pushed and shoved and yelped and howled and tried to stem the tide of dogs trying to come in.

For several seconds, there was a frenzied doggy whirlpool in Room 104 with Julia Fairhurst, Sandra Simmons, Gordon Threadneedle, Leslie Archway and Count Alucard himself caught up in the centre of the maelstrom and struggling to remain on their feet.

The tide turned at last. The avalanche doubled back on itself. Granville Cazelot and Archie Oliver, leading the charge along the corridor outside Room 104, were suddenly confronted with a huge tidal wave of dogs. Unable to retreat because of the weight of folk behind them, the Customs chief and the police inspector were bowled over by the canine onrush and then almost trodden underfoot by advancing dog owners, Car boot Sale persons, Jigsaw Puzzlers, Aquarists and several irate stallholders from the Handicrafts Fayre who had tagged along at the back.

By the time that Cazelot and Oliver had managed to struggle back onto their feet, both the dogs and the vampire count had gone again. A door at the far end of the corridor swung slowly shut to indicate the route that they had taken.

"Policewoman Simmons? Sergeant Threadgold? Detective Constable Archway? What are you three doing in Laburnum Towers?" asked a puzzled Archie Oliver, recognising the three members of the police force who had been left behind by the surging mass of dogs.

"Are you all right, Julia?" asked Ronnie Fairhurst struggling to the forefront of the vampire-hunters as his wife, who had also been swept out of Room 104 on the tide of dogs, attempted to recover her composure. "What happened?" continued Ronnie, offering his arm.

"No time for explanations now!" snapped Granville Cazelot. "Let's get after those dogs while the trail's still hot."

But, from that point on, the scent of both the missing dogs and the Transylvanian vampire count went strangely cool.

Beckoning the vampire-hunting volunteers forward, Cazelot and Oliver led the way along the

173

white-tiled basement corridor at Laburnum Towers.

Having failed to pick up the trail on the first floor, Police Inspector Oliver had instantly despatched Sergeant Threadneedle and Detective Constable Archway down to the lobby with orders to position guards at all of the hotel's exits. Having thus ensured – or so they hoped – that neither the vampire nor the dogs could leave the building, Oliver and Cazelot had led their forces up to the top of the hotel and then systematically combed every floor – so far without success.

All that remained for them to search was the basement which contained the Laburnum Towers Leisure Centre Complex.

Behind Cazelot and Oliver came Customs Officers Wilkins, Fairhurst and Hargreaves (in his fleecy-lined tartan slippers), with Policewoman Simmons close at hand. Following these officers were the dog owners, the Car Boot Sale people, the Jigsaw Puzzlers and the Aquarists – in no particular order, for each and every one of them felt that the safest place to be was in the middle of the party.

Although the white-walled basement was well lit, it was curiously quiet. There was not one single vampire-hunter, officers included, who did not feel some nervousness at the prospect of encountering a pointy-toothed, pale-complexioned, long-legged vampire around every corner. But corners came and went without sight or sound of either the vampire or the dogs.

"This is a total waste of time," growled Granville Cazelot. "They're not down here, Archie."

"We haven't searched in there yet," replied the police inspector, nodding towards the entrance to the swimming-pool which lay some twenty metres or so ahead.

"We don't *need* to search in there, Archie," snapped Cazelot. Then, coming to a halt and holding up a hand to signal for stillness among the ranks, he added: "Listen! What can you hear?"

There were two porthole-type windows in the double-doors through which the two men could see the rippling greeny-ghostly glow from the underwater lighting reflected on the swimming-pool's ceiling and accentuating the eerie silence.

"N-n-n-nothing, Granville," said Archie Oliver, giving an involuntary shiver.

"Exactly!" snapped Cazelot. "We're looking for a hundred dogs who are in pursuit of a vampire. They're *dogs*, Archie, by name and nature. Dogs bark. 'Woof-woof!' At least, my Wolf does, when he's after something. I can't speak for your prissy poodle – it wouldn't surprise me if she 'miaowed'!"

"Trixiebelle barks well enough, when it's needed, Granville," replied Oliver stoutly. "She'll make as much noise as your Alsatian, if it's called for – you mark my words."

"German Shepherd dog!" growled the Customs chief, correcting his companion. "We're only wasting valuable time down here. One way or another, that evil· monster's managed to escape from the hotel. I'm calling off the indoor search and organising another one outside. You stay here and search the swimming-pool if that's what you want to do."

175

With which, the Customs chief turned and shouldered his way through the volunteers who, one by one, turned and followed him back the way that they had come. Police Inspector Oliver was left quite alone staring fearfully through the porthole windows at the spooky green glow that lay beyond.

"Wait for me, Granville!" the police inspector called and his words echoed along the basement corridor. "I'm coming with you!"

And he did.

12

Inside the hotel swimming-pool, a hundred dogs and more lay obediently still and silent around all four sides of the pool, their heads turned enquiringly towards Count Alucard who was sitting, deep in thought, on the end of the diving-board.

Some minutes before, having heard the approaching vampire-hunters, the Count had called out, in Transylvanian, a single word of command and the dogs, who had been frisking in the water, had doggy-paddled to the sides, clambered out, shaken themselves, and assumed the statuesque positions they were holding now.

He had managed to fool his pursuers yet again, the Count told himself, but for how long this time? And how long would it be before someone else came down into the basement and did not shy from walking through the swimming-pool doors?

Not long at all, as things turned out. In fact, barely thirty more seconds were to pass before a face peered in at one of the portholes and then the doors swung open.

"Hello, Count Alucard!"

"Henry Hollins!" cried the Count, leaping

joyfully to his feet. "My dear, *good* friend! But how did you know to look for me down here?"

"I know that when you're at home, in Castle Alucard, and you want to hide from people, you always go down to the dungeons – I took a chance and came down to the lowest part of the hotel – and here you are."

"But what stroke of fortune has brought you to Laburnum Towers?"

"It's a long story. . . ."

Henry Hollins made his explanations as brief as possible, quickly telling the Count about his father's latest fad for magic tricks and also about the Magic Convention which was taking place in the hotel.

"A Magical Convention?" exclaimed the Count. "Then all of those gentlemen dressed like me – or otherwise curiously garbed – are merely magicians on the spree?"

"That's right."

"And the blood-stained guillotine and the sinister Chinese cabinet are nothing more nor less than conjurors' harmless props . . .?"

"*Help!*" A muffled voice interrupted the Count's musings and seemed to be coming from somewhere beyond the far end of the swimming-pool. "Is somebody out there? *Please!* I need assistance!"

Count Alucard and Henry Hollins exchanged a puzzled glance and then set off together in the direction that the sound came from. They arrived at a door which had a sign above it saying: FITNESS CENTRE. As Henry and the Count

178

went through the door, the dogs clambered onto their paws, shook themselves again, and padded silently after them.

"That must be the sinister Chinese cabinet you mentioned," said Henry, nodding at the tall, red-painted wooden box, decorated with gold signs, which was standing in the middle of the Fitness Centre, surrounded by lifting-weights and exercise bicycles.

"Who's there?" the voice said nervously from inside the cabinet.

"You're Ashley, aren't you?" said Count Alucard, recognising the voice as the one belonging to the man dressed as a Chinese mandarin he had seen earlier that afternoon.

"Who wants to know? Have I met you?"

"Briefly. We travelled in the lift together. I am Count Alucard from Transylvania. This young man with me is Henry Hollins, a dear, good friend. Now that we have told you who we are, perhaps you would be so kind as to show yourself?"

"I only wish I could, chum!" There was a note of desperation in the voice. "But I'm stuck inside this flipping cabinet!"

"Who locked you in?" asked Henry Hollins.

"It was my own silly, stupid fault entirely. I came down here to practise my famous Chinese Cabinet escape illusion in private. But the front part locked tight when I got in and the secret panel, at the back, that I used to make my escape, has jammed fast." There was a pause of several seconds as the prisoner rattled the inside of the cabinet in an attempt to break free, but without success.

179

"Trust me to make a hash of things."

"I assure you, sir, there is no cause for concern. My young friend will seek out the hotel's handyman who will force the lock. We'll have you out, safe and sound, in two shakes of a werewolf's tail."

"That won't be soon enough," wailed Ashley. "I'm supposed to be performing this illusion in front of all my fellow magicians in five minutes from now. If the cabinet's been forced open, I won't be able to use it. What am I to do? A magician locked inside his own escape illusion! I shall be a laughing-stock in the world of magic."

"Perhaps there is another solution to your unfortunate predicament," said the Count. "But it will mean leaving you here, locked in that cabinet and on your own for a little while longer."

"No problem," replied Ashley. "I've been in worse situations. I was locked inside a mail-sack once, bound and handcuffed, that I failed to escape from – this is *much* more comfortable."

"Good," said the Count. "And you won't be entirely on your own. I shall leave the dogs here with you."

"Dogs? What dogs?"

"A few canine friends of mine. Well – just over a hundred of them, in actual fact. But they're *very* well behaved. It would serve to comfort them though, while we are gone, if you would oblige me by murmuring the odd kind word at them through your cabinet."

"Anything! Anything! But where are you going? What are you going to do?"

181

"I intend to go up onto the stage myself and make your apologies. I shall say that you have been unavoidably detained. . ."

"But that won't help at all!" Ashley's voice rose agitatedly. "They won't be satisfied with apologies – not those chaps – they will start to make investigations. . ."

"Pray calm yourself, my friend, I do beseech you! Allow me to finish. It is also my intention, with the assistance of my young friend, Henry, to take your place. I shall show your magicians a little illusion of my own that will serve to make them forget your absence."

"You will?" Ashley's voice sounded a little puzzled. "Can you do magic tricks then?"

"I am an 'Alucard'!" the Count said proudly, pulling himself up to his full height then, with a wink at Henry Hollins, he added: "I can do magic."

"By golly gumbo, Archie!" cried Granville Cazelot, smashing his clenched right fist into his open left hand. "We've got the evil rotter!"

"Who?"

"Dracula, you silly man!"

"Where?"

"Over there!"

The pair were standing in the hotel lobby which they intended to commandeer as the operations-room for the reorganised vampire-hunt. Cazelot was insisting on carrying out his scheme for extending the hunt's boundaries outside the hotel's perimeter to take in the woods and fields beyond.

182

But if what the Customs officer had just said was true, there would be no need to look any further. Archie Oliver looked across the lobby at where Cazelot was pointing.

"That's not the vampire, Granville," said Oliver, disappointed. "That's just his empty coffin."

The smart, black polished coffin was being wheeled across the busy lobby on a porter's trolley by Kevin Protheroe.

"Believe me, Archie, wherever that coffin goes, you may be sure that its evil owner won't be far away. He's a *vampire*. All vampires are lost without their coffins – they take them everywhere. Don't you watch the late-night movies on the telly? Come on. We'll follow it. I'll bet you a cup of tea and a slice of swiss-roll that it leads us straight to the blackhearted villain it belongs to."

Not long after, the police officer and the Customs chief were standing in the Laburnum Lounge, which was doing duty as a theatre, where every seat was taken up by magicians and their wives all waiting for the curtain to rise on the early evening magic show. Cazelot and Oliver would have preferred to have followed the coffin which had gone backstage, but the surly attendant at the entrance door had been insistent that they remain where they were, at the very back of the lounge.

"Don't you know who I am?" the Customs chief had blustered. "I'm Chief Customs Officer Cazelot."

"And I'm Police Inspector Oliver."

"I don't care if you're Laurel and Hardy," the attendant had sourly informed them. "Nobody gets to go backstage at a magic show except magicians – them's the rules."

And, rather than argue with the man, the two officers had decided to do as they had been instructed – and to bide their time and wait and see what happened next. There was an excited buzz coming up from the audience of magicians. The evening promised to be an exciting one.

Emily Hollins, who was sitting with her husband in the centre of the lounge, would have been looking forward to the entertainment with more enthusiasm had Henry deigned to put in an appearance.

"Where do you think he's got to, Albert?" asked Mrs Hollins, giving a worried glance at the empty seat at her side.

"I don't know, Emily. You know what Henry's like. He's forever going off and getting himself into some sort of pickle or another. He'll turn up – when it takes his fancy. Speaking for myself, I'm going to forget about young Henry and enjoy the show." Then, as the lights began to dim in the lounge, Albert glanced at his programme and whispered to his wife: "It's a Chinese magician who's on first – performing the Celebrated Chinese Cabinet Illusion."

There was a burst of anticipatory applause from the magical fraternity as the curtain began to rise. But the applause faded into murmurs of disappointment as the stage revealed a totally unexpected sight.

"That's not a sinister Chinese cabinet, Albert –
it's a coffin!" murmured Emily to her husband,
voicing the unspoken opinions of most of the
members of the audience.

Count Alucard's sleek black coffin was standing
upright, bathed in spotlights, centre stage. A
moment later, a figure familiar to both Emily and
Albert Hollins entered from the wings.

"And that's not a Chinese magician neither,
Emily," said Albert Hollins, a trifle disgruntled.
"It's our Henry, the cheeky little monkey!
Whatever does he imagine he is up to – hogging
all the limelight? It's me that's the magician in our
family."

"I wish I'd known that he was going to go up on
the stage, Albert," whispered Emily Hollins. "I'd
have brought a clean shirt along for him to put
on."

"L-l-l-ladies and gentlemen," stammered Henry,
suffering a slight case of collywobbles in his
stomach – then, gaining in confidence, he
continued: "First, I have a rather sad
announcement – Ashley, the Chinese mandarin
magician, has been unavoidably detained elsewhere
and will not be performing his celebrated Chinese
Cabinet Illusion for you this evening . . ." Henry
paused until the disappointed murmurs had died
away, before continuing, " . . .However, it is my
proud pleasure to introduce a noble gentleman
who has come all the way from Transylvania to
entertain you – the amazing, the fantastic – Count
Alucard!"

Holding his black cloak outstretched displaying

its crimson lining, Count Alucard strode out onto the stage and then stood quite still, his pale face looking even paler in the footlights' glow. The audience, appreciating this dramatic entrance and believing themselves in the presence of an international magician, clapped enthusiastically. Count Alucard, unused to receiving such a show of warmth, basked in the applause.

"It's him, Archie! It's the blood-guzzling monster!" gulped Granville Cazelot at the back of the lounge.

"Shall we nip up and arrest him now, Granville?" whispered the police inspector. "I think I've got a pair of handcuffs in the glove compartment of the car."

"Not yet," replied the Customs chief. "He'd turn and make a break for it if he saw us coming.

'Softlee, softlee, catchee monkey.' We'll wait and make our move when the time is ripe."

"Ladies and gentlemen," began the Count, when the applause had died away. "With the aid of my young assistant and good friend, Henry Hollins, I am going to perform for you tonight the Celebrated Transylvanian Coffin Illusion." The announcement was greeted with a gasp of amazement. The Laburnum Lounge was packed with magicians but not one of them had ever seen – or even heard of – the Celebrated Transylvanian Coffin Illusion. "But first," continued the Count, "I shall require the assistance of two members of the audience."

"This is it, Archie – the time's ripe *now*!" gloated Granville Cazelot then, raising a hand, he called out: "My companion and I would be glad to assist you, sir!"

With Archie Oliver scurrying along behind him, the Customs chief strode down the aisle between the packed rows of chairs.

"I wonder," began Count Alucard, when the two men had clambered up onto the stage, "whether you would be kind enough to tell me your first names?"

"I'm Granville," said Cazelot with a silly smirk.

"And I'm Archibald," said Oliver, with a smarmy grin.

"Excellent!" Count Alucard beamed at the pair as he turned and indicated the upright coffin. "Well then, Granville and Archibald, I wonder if you would both be so kind as to examine this casket?" He paused as the two hastened to oblige, and added: "Make sure that it hasn't got a false bottom or that there aren't any secret panels."

"He's playing right into our hands, Archie!" Granville Cazelot hissed gleefully at Archie Oliver as the two men examined the coffin carefully on all four sides. "This thing's as safe as the Bank of England. If he's daft enough to get inside it, we've got the blighter bang to rights."

"Are you both satisfied, gentlemen, that this is a genuine coffin?" asked the Count. "And that there is no way in or out of it except by way of the lid?"

"Absolutely!" cried Cazelot across the footlights, hiding a grin of triumph.

"Positively!" called Oliver into the audience, stifling a chuckle.

"Good." Count Alucard turned and tugged at the coffin-lid which opened easily. There were 'Oooohs' and 'Aaaahs' of admiration from all around the lounge as the audience was treated to a first glimpse of the rich satin-lined interior with the silk embroidered pillow at the top. "And now, once I am safely contained within," the Count continued to the audience, "my assistant, Henry Hollins, will close the lid securely." Count Alucard stepped inside the coffin and stood upright. "And when you have done so, my dear young friend," he whispered to Henry, "count slowly up to twenty under your breath and then open it again."

As instructed, Henry carefully closed the coffin-lid. Cazelot and Oliver had positioned themselves on either side.

"One, two, three . . ." began Henry Hollins to himself.

"Ladies and gentlemen!" Granville Cazelot's

voice thundered out into the auditorium. "We have reason to believe that the person confined inside this coffin is an impostor. He is not a magician at all – he's a vampire!"

This time, the audience's 'Oooohs' and 'Aaaahs' were ones of horror.

"There is no cause for concern," called Oliver. "I am a police inspector and my companion is a chief Customs officer. It is our intention to take the monster into custody. As luck would have it, I have a pair of handcuffs in the glove compartment of my—"

"— eighteen, nineteen, twenty," muttered Henry Hollins under his breath and, as he did so, he tugged open the coffin-lid.

"Ooooooh!" "Aaaaah!"

There could be no doubt about it. The satin-lined, silk-pillowed coffin was empty. Count Alucard had vanished.

"He's gone!" gasped Granville Cazelot.

"It's magic!" cried Archie Oliver.

"Of course it is!" called one of a trio of bald-headed, rosy-cheeked portly magicians sitting in the audience.

"Good old Archie!" cried another.

"Well done, Granville!" cried the third. "You certainly had us fooled!"

But the three portly magicians were not alone in thinking that the 'vampire announcement' had been part and parcel of Count Alucard's act. One by one, the members of the audience rose to their feet and started to applaud. In seconds, the entire lounge was standing, clapping and cheering. They had never before seen anything like the Celebrated Transylvanian Coffin Illusion. They would never see its like again.

But Granville Cazelot and Archie Oliver were not admiring of Count Alucard's magic.

"I've had enough of this malarkey, Archie," muttered Cazelot, giving the empty coffin another nervous glance. "How are we supposed to apprehend a monster that can make itself invisible?"

"Where do you think it's got to, Granville?" asked Archie Oliver giving an uneasy glance over his shoulder.

"I don't know, Archie. But I *do* know this much: I'm not waiting to find out. I'm not hanging about in this place for him to stick his invisible pointy teeth into my neck."

With which, Chief Customs Officer Cazelot leaped over the footlights, down into the auditorium and set off, briskly, along the central aisle towards the door marked 'Exit'. Police Inspector Archie Oliver was no more than a couple of paces behind his friend.

Up on the stage, as the wild applause grew even wilder, Henry Hollins, the magician's proud assistant, took bow – after bow – after bow – after bow. . . .

"What *I* still don't understand, Count," said Emily Hollins as she poured out cups of tea for Albert, Henry and herself, "is how you managed to vanish out of that coffin?"

"What do you think, Henry?" asked Count Alucard, his dark eyes twinkling. "Should we let your mother in on our little secret?"

"That's entirely up to you, Count," said Henry Hollins who, if truth be known, had not the faintest idea as to how his Transylvanian friend had managed to do his magic.

The Gala Magic Show had ended. The stalls in the Laburnum Towers ballroom had been taken down. The 1000 magicians had gone, taking with them their plastic bags bulging with new tricks. Count Alucard and Emily, Albert and Henry Hollins, were having a night-time snack in the Candlelight Cafeteria before they, too, would have to take their leave of each other.

"You shouldn't have asked Count Alucard to tell you how he did it, Emily," admonished Albert. "A magician should never reveal his secrets. That's one of the first rules of the Magic Circle. Isn't that

191

so, Count?"

"I do believe that is the considered view of the magical fraternity, Mr Hollins," replied the Count. "However, as there were neither magician's skills nor trickery employed in my illusion – I think we might, on this occasion, stretch the rules and tell Emily how I effected the little deceit."

"Yes, *please*," said Emily Hollins, leaning forward eagerly over the red-checked tablecloth.

"My dear Emily – it was all too easy. It was evening when the Gala Show began. As soon as afternoon has turned to dusk, my vampire's powers allow me to turn myself into a bat. Which is exactly what I did the moment Henry closed the lid of my coffin. When the lid was opened, I was concealed, hanging upside-down, behind the pillow."

"Oh. So *that's* how you did it," said Emily, sounding just a little disappointed.

"You see?" the Count continued with a wry smile. "Albert was right. A magician should never reveal his secrets. Magic tricks are not half as intriguing once their secrets are common knowledge." He paused, nodded gravely at each one of them in turn, and then continued: "I cannot tell you how utterly delightful it has been to see you all again – but now, if you'll excuse me. . . ."

"Do you *have* to go, Count?" asked Henry, sadly. "You're safe now. The vampire-hunters have moved on somewhere else."

"But when they fail to find me 'somewhere else', Henry – they will undoubtedly come back here and start all over again. One of the burdens I am forced to bear in life, my young friend, is the fact that vampire-hunters are distressingly persistent people. It would not do for the three of you to be seen with me. Before I go, I would deem it extremely gracious if you would grant me one small favour?"

"If there is anything that we can do for you, Count," said Emily, "you know that you only have to ask."

"I've decided to fly back to Transylvania on my own two wings. Passing through that airport caused me more than enough problems. But I'm afraid I'm going to have to leave my coffin behind. I wonder whether I might trouble you to take care of it – until my next visit?"

Albert Hollins tried not to frown. He could envisage some slight problems that might arise from keeping a Transylvanian vampire's coffin in a small semi-detached house. But Emily had no qualms whatsoever.

"We'd be delighted to look after it for you," Mrs Hollins announced. "If you're quite sure you can manage without it?"

"Oh yes, indeed! I've been intending to treat myself to a new one for some time past. I've often thought that it was time that I became a 'two-coffin' man. There's a particularly tempting model in this month's edition of *The Coffin-Makers' Journal*. And, if I kept a spare one over here – I've put my clothes and things back into it – it would mean that I could pop over and visit you quite frequently."

"Yes, *please*, Count!" said Henry Hollins.

"We'll consider that settled then. And now, if

you will forgive me, there is a pleasurable task I must perform before I set wing for Castle Alucard. . . ." The Count paused and slapped the palm of his slim hand against his pale forehead. "On my grandfather's grave! There are *two* tasks to be performed – in all the excitement caused by our theatrical triumph, Henry, I had quite forgotten about Ashley's sad plight. I must attend to his release from the sinister Chinese cabinet *immediately*."

13

On dark outstretched membraneous wing, Count Alucard skimmed over the countryside which bordered the town. Gliding on currents of warm night air, he sensed rather than saw the hundred and more dogs that were racing along beneath him.

The Count had promised himself that, before returning them to their rightful owners, he would afford his new-found friends the same sort of treat that so delighted the wolves in the Forest of Tolokovin.

The dogs were certainly relishing their moonlight romp. Billy Bonzo, Wolf and Alistair, a broad-chested Labrador, bounded along in the forefront while, as always, Ching-Ching, Wan-Toon and Hermann, the dachshund, brought up the rear. Haring across meadow and stream, scampering through thicket and sometimes woodland bracken, leaping over or under stiles and fences, the dogs went gleefully through the moonlit night wherever the Count chose to lead them.

For half an hour at least, they felt themselves to be *real* animals – not housebound pampered show-dog pets.

★ ★ ★

Monty Wilson whistled jauntily through his teeth as he slipped Benjamin Disraeli into pride of place on the middle shelf of the display cabinet, already crammed with all manner of corkscrews, in the living-room.

"That *is* a nice one, Monty," said Freda Wilson, who did not usually compliment her cabbie husband on his additions to the corkscrew collection.

"It was a bargain too," said the cabbie then, sensing that his wife had also had an enjoyable day, he added: "How are the decorations in the bathroom coming along?"

"Go take a peep. I've got my eye on some curtain material that will just match that duck-egg blue."

"Well done that woman," said Monty Wilson. "I thought I might nip out in an hour or so and fetch us back a Chinese takeaway."

"Scrummy!"

Steven Wilkins took off his blazer with its Aquarium Club badge on the pocket and hung it, carefully, on a hanger in the wardrobe. He took off his Aquarium Club tie, with its goldfish motif, and hung that up carefully too.

Then, taking the tropical fish suppliers catalogue out of his raincoat pocket, the Customs officer crossed into the sitting-room, which was lined with fish tanks, switched on the ceiling-light, sat down in his favourite armchair and browsed through the catalogue.

The reward that he would get from the stamp

dealer when he returned the rare, unused Lithuanian stamp would be more than sufficient for him to treat his fish to all manner of bits and pieces: little mermaids perched on plastic rocks, combing their golden hair; plastic deep-sea divers letting out real bubbles; pirate treasure chests overflowing with plastic gold and jewels – and, best of all perhaps, miniature plastic castles with open portcullises which the smaller fish could swim through.

Fantastic!

Getting out of the chair, Stevie Wilkins crossed and turned off the ceiling light. He did not need it. Every fish tank in the room was furnished with its own interior illumination. The Customs officer went back to his chair and sighed contentedly as he basked in the shimmering greeny glow which bathed the room.

"Ronnie?" said Julia Fairhurst who had been gazing into the flickering gas-fire flames for several minutes, plucking up the courage to put her question.

"Yes, Julia? What is it?"

"Would you mind *very* much if I became a regular member of The Whodunnit Club?"

"Of course not, Julia. Why should I?"

"I just wondered if you might?" said Julia, giving a little shrug. "Only I *did* enjoy myself this afternoon. And it does seem such a shame that they're so short of members. You never know – if I started going, someone else might start going, and it could pick up in no time."

"It might," agreed Ronnie Fairhurst. "And while you are at your Whodunnit Club, I could go to the Jigsaw Puzzlers. Then you and I could meet up afterwards and go for a hamburger, or a pizza, or some pasta – or something of that ilk."

"Why not?"

"What about the spice-rack, Julia?"

"What about the spice-rack?"

"Well – are you still dead keen on my putting it together tonight?"

"Oh, let's leave it until tomorrow, Ronnie. I was wondering whether you might fancy a cup of coffee? I'm going to make one for myself."

"Could I have cocoa instead? And could I have a ginger biccie?"

"You can have whatever your heart desires, Ronnie."

"Whizzo!"

Arthur Cresswell, the Jigsaw Puzzlers Club secretary, gazed without expression at the 30,000 and then some jigsaw puzzle pieces he had tipped out of the cardboard packing-case onto the sitting-room carpet.

"Whatever are you going to do with that lot, Arthur?" asked Sylvia Cresswell nervously.

"I'm going to sort them out, Sylvia," began Mr Cresswell, "into their separate puzzles and then I shall return them to their original boxes."

"My goodness me, Arthur! That's a challenge."

"I like a challenge," said Arthur Cresswell. He

stooped and picked up a single bit of jigsaw puzzle and studied it carefully. It could have come from Dr Livingstone's jacket – or it might have been a piece from one of several boxes to do with Animals And Their Place In Jigsaw Puzzles.

"I like a man to have a hobby," said Mrs Cresswell.

Only one table was occupied in the Hawaiian Bar at the Laburnum Towers hotel. Sandra Simmons and Hilton Hargreaves, who had separately succeeded in slipping away unnoticed from the vampire-hunt, had bumped into each other in the hotel foyer. They had found each other's company so entertaining that they were loathe to say 'goodnight'. Instead, they sipped through plastic straws at exotic drinks which had been served to them in scooped-out pineapples by a waitress called Sharon Pawson who was wearing a grass skirt. Hilton Hargreaves had fallen silent for several minutes.

"Is something bothering you, Hilton?" asked Sandra Simmons.

"I would have liked to have escorted you to your front door this evening, Sandra!" burst out the young Customs officer.

"There's nothing in the world to stop you," said the policewoman shyly.

"I don't know whether it might have escaped your notice," confessed the Customs officer, "but I'm wearing fleecy-lined tartan slippers."

"No, I hadn't noticed," replied Sandra, glancing

underneath the table. "I think they suit you," she added without the hint of a smile.

"You don't think they make me look like a bit of a gubbins?"

"I don't think that you could look like a 'bit of a gubbins' if you tried," said Sandra Simmons.

"*Really*?"

"Really."

"Come on then," said Hilton Hargreaves rising to his slippered feet and proffering the green-eyed, freckle-faced young policewoman his arm. "Let's go see about a bus."

In the glare of the searchlight beam from underneath the police helicopter which had located them, the hundred and more dogs sat patiently in the otherwise deserted quarry as their leg-weary owners walked towards them.

The dog owners had long since tired of being vampire-hunters. They were only grateful at being reunited with their pets.

"I can't imagine how the crafty, evil being managed to lure them out to this place, Archie," grumbled Chief Customs Officer Granville Cazelot.

"Nor me, Granville," said Police Inspector Oliver.

"More like a flipping canine Pied Piper than a blood-drinking monster, Archie."

There was no more time for conversation. All across the quarry, dogs were leaping up and bounding forward for tongue-licking, tail-wagging

reunions with their owners. Wolf, the German Shepherd dog, having recognised his master, was taking giant strides towards the Customs chief. At one and the same moment, Trixiebelle the Third was making an excited bee-line for Archie Oliver.

"Good boy! Good dog!" cried Granville Oliver as he ruffled hard the fur on top of Wolf's head.

"Stop it! Stop it, you silly old sausage!" cried Archie Oliver as Trixiebelle the Third very nearly bowled him over as she leaped up and struck him hard on the chest.

While both Wolf and Trixiebelle – indeed, all of the dogs – had loved every moment of their excursion with the Transylvanian vampire, at the end of the day, they recognised that there was nothing that could compete with a full dinner bowl.

"Eeny-meeny-miny-mo," said Albert Hollins as he dealt four playing cards, face down and in a row, onto the coffin lid.

Emily and Henry Hollins, sitting on the sofa in the living-room at 42 Nicholas Nickleby Close, Stapleford, were watching Albert proudly perform the new and expensive card trick he had bought at the magic convention.

Emily had decided that Count Alucard's coffin would suit admirably as a coffee table. The coffin's well-polished black wood was a perfect match for the upright piano which stood against the living-room wall. Emily could not wait to invite her next-door neighbours in for a coffee-morning to show off her latest acquisition.

"Point to a card, Emily," said Albert Hollins. "Any card."

"That one," said Emily, pointing to the second card in the face-down row of four.

"And which card were you thinking of?" asked Albert.

"The Queen of Hearts," said Emily.

"And there is that very lady!" announced Albert Hollins dramatically.

Albert turned over the card which Emily was pointing at. It wasn't the Queen of Hearts at all – it was the Seven of Clubs.

"I thought you said the trick was foolproof, Dad?" said Henry Hollins.

"It is," said Mr Hollins grumpily. "It just needs a bit of practice."

"Ah-Whooo-OOOH . . .!"

Somewhere nearby a stray mongrel was barking into the night. The sound reminded Henry Hollins of the way the wolves howled in the far-off Forest of Tolokovin. He crossed to the window, drew back the curtain and peered up at the star-spangled sky.

High up, over the little town of Stapleford – far *too* high for human eye to see – the small furry-bodied black fruit-eating vampire bat was gliding on outstretched wings, headed towards the south of England. It was a long way to the coast and a much longer distance to Transylvania, but Count Alucard was unconcerned. He was not in any hurry.

If dawn should chance to break before he arrived at Dover, he would sleep through the daylight hours in some disused barn or, perhaps, an ivy-covered belfry. When the next night came, he would hitch a lift aboard a cross-channel ferry. With favourable winds, accommodating air currents and a smattering of good fortune, he would be back at Castle Alucard within the week.

Count Alucard wondered idly whether there might be early snow, burdening the branches of the pine trees in the Forest of Tolokovin? Whether there might be ice-bound crystal streams to cross?

One thing was positive, the wolves that roamed the Forest of Tolokovin – his children of the night – would be more than glad to see him. And he would be more than glad to see them too.